A REVISED KEY TO THE

CASELESS CADDIS LARVAE
OF THE BRITISH ISLES

with notes on their ecology

by

J. M. EDINGTON*

and

A. G. HILDREW†

FRESHWATER BIOLOGICAL ASSOCIATION
SCIENTIFIC PUBLICATION No. 53

1995

Series Editor: J. M. ELLIOTT

* 3 Elm Grove Road, Whitchurch, Cardiff CF4 2BW, Wales.
† School of Biological Sciences, Queen Mary & Westfield College, University of London, Mile
  End Road, London, E1 4NS, England.

The National Rivers Authority (NRA) welcomes the opportunity to part-sponsor publication of *A Revised Key to the Caseless Caddis Larvae of the British Isles*, the latest in the FBA's series of Scientific Publications which continue to provide essential authoritative information needed to underpin the management of freshwater habitats. The publication is particularly relevant to the NRA because the caseless caddis include a number of taxa that are used to assess water quality by biological means.

The key and associated notes represent an invaluable source reference for identification, distribution and ecology. High quality information is required to maximise the effectiveness of measures to assess and monitor the state of rivers as part of the Authority's aim to achieve a continuing improvement in the water environment in England and Wales. Moreover, accurate identification of rarer macroinvertebrates is essential with respect to the Authority's duty to further conservation.

The NRA strongly recommends this FBA publication to practitioners and enthusiasts alike, but the NRA accepts no responsibility whatsoever for any errors or mis-statements contained in this publication. Any queries or comments should be directed to the FBA.

Published by the Freshwater Biological Association,
The Ferry House, Far Sawrey, Ambleside, Cumbria LA22 0LP

ISBN 0 900386 55 X

ISSN 0367-1887

PREFACE

In 1981 the FBA published the first of its two keys for identifying the larvae of caddisflies in the British Isles. The key brought together, for the first time, means for identifying all but a few of the non-casebearing species of caddis known to exist in the British Isles, written by Drs J. M. Edington and A. G. Hildrew. Their key was an immediate success and, since its publication, demand for it has steadily grown, not least because this group of insects commonly occur in a wide variety of freshwater habitats and their modes of life, including the herbivorous net-spinners and some free-ranging carnivores, are particularly fascinating. Additionally, this group of insects forms an important part of the biological assessment and classification of rivers in the UK, and the correct identification of the taxa included in this key now has considerable economic and practical importance.

For some time now the first edition of the key has been out of print, and we are exceedingly fortunate that Dr Edington and Professor Hildrew have been able to revise extensively their key for this completely new edition. With one exception *(Wormaldia mediana)* it includes all of the species known to occur in the British Isles, and the key is accompanied by detailed taxonomic notes that take account of recent studies made on the continent of Europe. Similarly, the sections on distribution and ecology have also been critically revised. The inclusion of ecological notes in our recent Scientific Publications has proved to be a popular feature, as has the provision of a detailed bibliography.

We are most grateful to the National Rivers Authority for part-sponsoring the publication of this new edition, which will be of value to those who use caddis larvae as part of their work on water quality and conservation. Its publication should also stimulate further research into the distribution and ecological requirements of species that until now have been difficult or impossible to identify. I hope that all will welcome this latest publication in the Association's series.

The Ferry House
April 1995

J. M. Elliott
Series Editor

CONTENTS

INTRODUCTION

To most people the word "caddis" conjures up a picture of an aquatic insect living inside a transportable case which it has constructed from sand particles, small stones or plant fragments. Indeed, it has been suggested (Hickin 1967) that the word may derive from the habit, once practised by travelling salesmen, of pinning samples of braid and ribbons or "cadace" to their coats. It is less generally known that there are substantial numbers of caddis larvae (46 species listed for Britain) which never make transportable cases. Some (the Hydropsychidae, Polycentropodidae, Ecnomidae and Philopotamidae) are associated with silk nets (Figs 156–166) which they use to collect food. Others (the Psychomyiidae), live principally within meandering galleries constructed on rock surfaces (Plate 1B, p. 83) and the members of one family (the Rhyacophilidae) are free-moving predators.

Our treatment of this somewhat diverse assemblage falls into two sections. In the first section we have provided, in the form of a key (pp. 11–53) and an associated taxonomic commentary (pp. 54–75), the information necessary to identify caseless caddis species. In the second section (pp. 75–120) we have summarised the information currently available on various aspects of the ecology and general biology of the group. This latter account deals with feeding biology, habitat distribution and life histories. With this group of caddis, as with other invertebrates, detailed ecological studies were able to get underway only when the taxonomic problems had been resolved; a point worth stressing when taxonomic work seems to have fallen out of fashion.

It may seem a very straightforward matter to distinguish caddis larvae with cases from those without them. Unfortunately, however, the process of collection, particularly by means of a net or other sampling device, frequently separates cased caddis from their cases. Similarly, net-spinners become separated from their nets and gallery-builders from their galleries. In the probable absence of such clues, the key has to deal initially with both cased and caseless larvae and to distinguish them on the basis of morphological features.

If it becomes evident that the specimen in question belongs to one of the case-bearing families, then the search will need to be continued using the companion key in the Freshwater Biological Association series (Wallace et al. 1990).

RECENT TAXONOMIC DEVELOPMENTS

Since the publication of the first edition of our key (Edington & Hildrew 1981), there have been some major advances in the taxonomic study of caseless caddis. Most notably the greatly increased volume of work from continental Europe has clarified many of the issues concerning the Hydropsychidae which remained unresolved in our previous key.

Contrary to our earlier view, Malicky (1984) has demonstrated that *Hydropsyche bulgaromanorum* Malicky 1977 occurred in Britain, at least until 1926. Subsequently, however, it may have become extinct. Previously it had been misidentified as *Hydropsyche guttata* Pictet 1834, a species which appears never to have been present in this country. The use of continental material and the description by Lecureuil et al. (1983) has allowed the inclusion of *H. bulgaromanorum* in our revised key.

Hydropsyche exocellata has not reappeared in Britain since early records of adults at the beginning of the century. However, the useful larval description by Jalón (1981) and material from France that we have been able to examine, has allowed us to include this species.

At the time of our previous key in 1981, *Hydropsyche saxonica* appeared to be an extremely rare species in Britain (Badcock 1976, 1977) and we were generally pessimistic about obtaining material for examination. However, since then the picture has changed dramatically. Nationwide studies of benthic invertebrates by the NERC's Institute of Freshwater Ecology (as part of the River Communities Project) have revealed that *H. saxonica* has a patchy but widespread distribution in England and Wales. Moreover, some useful commentaries on the distinguishing features of the larvae have been forthcoming from continental Europe, including Denmark (Wiberg-Larsen 1980), Norway (Bongard 1990; Bongard et al. 1991) and Germany (Pitsch 1993). It is now firmly established that the larvae resemble those of *Hydropsyche fulvipes* but with some important differences.

Continental work, especially by Pitsch (1993), has prompted us to look again at the means of separating *Rhyacophila dorsalis, R. obliterata* and *R. septentrionis* in the family Rhyacophilidae. Users of our previous key frequently reported difficulty with this group and consequently we have revised our treatment, on the basis of continental work and as a result of examining additional British material.

With the family Polycentropodidae the only significant development has been the discovery by Wallace & Wallace (1983) of the larvae of *Plectrocnemia brevis* McLachlan. In some respects this proves to be intermediate between the two more familiar species, *P. conspera* and *P. geniculata*. Consequently the section of the key relating to *Plectrocnemia* needed to be revised radically. Otherwise the polycentropodid section follows Edington (1964).

In the family Philopotamidae, the larvae of *Wormaldia mediana* are still undiscovered and, in fact, this remains the only gap in our coverage of the larvae of the caseless caddis species. We believe we have arrived at a means of separating the larvae of *Wormaldia occipitalis* and *W. subnigra*, however, an unresolved problem in the previous key.

The section of the key relating to the Psychomyiidae is based on Edington & Alderson (1973) and O'Connor & Wise (1980) and remains unaltered. This extremely interesting group of small caddis continues to receive little attention from biologists.

The identification of *Ecnomus tenellus*, the only British representative of the Economidae, presents no problems but we now have a somewhat clearer picture of its life-style (pp. 88, 103 and 116).

CHECKLIST OF CASELESS CADDIS IN THE BRITISH ISLES

The updated checklist of species (based on Barnard 1985) is presented below. Changed specific names are shown in brackets [ ].

Family and Genus   Species

RHYACOPHILIDAE

RHYACOPHILA Pictet, 1834   *dorsalis* (Curtis, 1834)   (1)
                                  munda McLachlan, 1862   (2)
                                  obliterata McLachlan, 1863   (3)
                                  septentrionis McLachlan, 1865[*] (4)

[*]Regarded as synonymous with *R. fasciata* Hagen by Malicky (1983) and Pitsch (1993)

PHILOPOTAMIDAE

PHILOPOTAMUS Stephens, 1829   *montanus* (Donovan, 1813)   (5)

WORMALDIA McLachlan, 1878   *mediana* McLachlan, 1878   (6)
                                  occipitalis (Pictet, 1834)   (7)
                                  subnigra McLachlan, 1865   (8)

CHIMARRA Stephens, 1829   *marginata* (Linnaeus, 1761)   (9)

PSYCHOMYIIDAE

LYPE McLachlan, 1878   *phaeopa* (Stephens, 1836)   (10)
                                  reducta (Hagen, 1868)   (11)

METALYPE Klapálek, 1898	*fragilis* (Pictet, 1834)	(12)
PSYCHOMYIA Latreille, 1829	*pusilla* (Fabricius, 1781)	(13)
TINODES Leach, 1815	*assimilis* McLachlan, 1865	(14)
	dives (Pictet, 1834)	(15)
	maclachani Kimmins, 1966	(16)
	[*aureolus*]	
	maculicornis (Pictet, 1834)	(17)
	pallidulus McLachlan, 1878	(18)
	rostocki McLachlan, 1878	(19)
	unicolor (Pictet, 1834)	(20)
	waeneri (Linnaeus, 1758)	(21)

ECNOMIDAE

| ECNOMUS McLachlan, 1864 | *tenellus* (Rambur, 1842) | (22) |

POLYCENTROPODIDAE

CYRNUS Stephens, 1836	*flavidus* McLachlan, 1864	(23)
	insolutus McLachlan, 1878	(24)
	trimaculatus (Curtis, 1834)	(25)
HOLOCENTROPUS McLachlan, 1878	*dubius* (Rambur, 1842)	(26)
	picicornis (Stephens, 1836)	(27)
	stagnalis (Albarda, 1874)	(28)
NEURECLIPSIS McLachlan, 1864	*bimaculata* (Linnaeus, 1758)	(29)
PLECTROCNEMIA McLachlan, 1836	*brevis* McLachlan, 1871	(30)
	conspersa (Curtis, 1834)	(31)
	geniculata McLachlan, 1871	(32)
POLYCENTROPUS Curtis, 1835	*flavomaculatus* (Pictet, 1834)	(33)
	irroratus (Curtis, 1835)	(34)
	[*multiguttatus*]	
	kingi McLachlan, 1881	(35)

HYDROPSYCHIDAE

| CHEUMATOPSYCHE Wallengren, 1891 | *lepida* (Pictet, 1834) | (36) |
| DIPLECTRONA Westwood, 1840 | *felix* McLachlan, 1878 | (37) |

HYDROPSYCHE Pictet, 1834   *angustipennis* (Curtis, 1834)   (38)
    bulgaromanorum Malicky, 1977   (39)
    [*guttata*]
    contubernalis McLachlan, 1865   (40)
    [*ornatula*]
    exocellata Dufour, 1841   (41)
    fulvipes (Curtis, 1834)   (42)
    instabilis (Curtis, 1834)   (43)
    [*fulvipes*]
    pellucidula (Curtis, 1834)   (44)
    saxonica McLachlan, 1884   (45)
    siltalai Döhler, 1963   (46)
    [*instabilis*]

The handbook by Macan (1973) is the most appropriate general work to use in identifying caddisfly adults. However, this should be replaced by Hildrew & Morgan (1974) when dealing with the Hydropsychidae, because this latter work takes account of the more recent taxonomic revisions of the family. Also the new key by Marshall (1978) supersedes the section in Macan's handbook dealing with the Hydroptilidae. Fisher (1977) has provided additional information on the adult females of the genus *Tinodes* (Psychomyiidae). The Atlas of European Trichoptera devised by Malicky (1983) illustrates the genitalia of British and European species in a standardised form which eases the task of making comparisons.

PRESERVATION AND EXAMINATION

Larvae for taxonomic investigation are usually preserved in 70 or 80% ethyl or isopropyl alcohol. Some taxonomists prefer more powerful fixatives such as Kahle's or Pampel's fluid which penetrate the specimen more rapidly. However, these should not be used for long-term preservation because they cause colour changes (for example, in the thoracic pigment patches of psychomyiid larvae). They also have the disadvantage of being more toxic and pungent.

The characters used in the key should be readily visible using a stereomicroscope at x50 magnification with spotlight illumination from above.

Where it is appropriate to mount a larval structure on a microscope slide for examination using a compound microscope at higher magnification (this is sometimes necessary with parts of psychomyiid larvae), a 50/50 mixture of glycerol and 70% alcohol provides a suitable temporary mountant. More permanent mounts can be made directly from alcohol-preserved specimens using gum chloral.

NOTES ON USE OF THE·KEY

Finally, some comments about the use of the key. We have included in the couplets what seem to be the most obvious and useful features, and in the first instance the specimen in question should be run straight through the key on this basis. When a provisional answer has been obtained, the taxonomic commentary (see pp. 54–75) apppropriate to that family should be read carefully. This will provide additional taxonomic features, warn of problems of variability of characters and their application to early instar larvae, and also mention life-history features or distribution patterns of potential diagnostic value. This additional information should be sufficient to confirm the original identification or to cast doubt on it. In the latter case another excursion through the key is indicated.

THE KEY

1   1st abdominal segment carries structures for supporting a case, which may take one of the following forms:
(a) Three fleshy protuberances, one dorsal, two lateral (Figs 2–4)—
     case bearer:- Families PHRYGANEIDAE, LIMNEPHILIDAE, MOLANNIDAE, BERAEIDAE, ODONTOCERIDAE, GOERIDAE*

(b) One dorsal protuberance and two lateral, plate-like pads (Figs 5–7)—
     case bearer:- Families LEPTOCERIDAE, SERICOSTOMATIDAE*

(c) Lateral fleshy protuberances only (Fig. 8)—
     case bearer:- Family LEPIDOSTOMATIDAE*

* Consult the key by Wallace et al. (1990) to identify larvae in the above Families.

—   None of these case-supporting structures is present on the 1st abdominal segment—   2

2   Distinct hard plates present on dorsal surface of 2nd and 3rd thoracic segments (Figs 20–24)—   7

—   No plates on dorsal surface of 2nd and 3rd thoracic segments (Figs 15–19)—   3

3   Tufted gills present on abdominal segments (Fig. 15)—
     Family RHYACOPHILIDAE (taxonomic notes, p. 54), 11

—   No tufted gills on abdominal segments (Figs 16–19)—   4

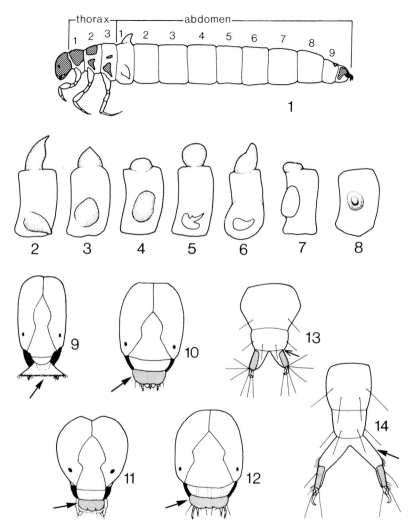

Figs 1–14.   **1**: generalised diagram of caddis larva to show segmentation of the body. **2–8**: lateral views of 1st abdominal segment in various families (anterior is to the left):- 2, Phryganeidae; 3, Limnephilidae; 4, Beraeidae; 5, 6, Leptoceridae; 7, Sericostomatidae; 8, Lepidostomatidae. **9–12**: head capsule (dorsal view, with labrum arrowed) of:- 9, Philopotamidae; 10, Psychomyiidae; 11, *Glossosoma* (Glossosomatidae); 12, Polycentropodidae. **13**: anal prolegs of Psychomyiidae, indicating absence of basal section (arrow). **14**: anal prolegs of Polycentropodidae, indicating long basal section (arrow).

4   Labrum principally composed of a transverse sclerotized plate* (Figs
     10–12, arrows)—   5

     * It is important here to ensure that it is the labrum which is being examined and not the
     anterior margin of the frontoclypeus.

—   Labrum neither sclerotized nor plate-like, but white and membranous
     with a brush-like anterior border (Fig. 9, arrow)—
                 Family PHILOPOTAMIDAE (taxonomic notes, p. 56), 13

5   Lateral plates on 2nd and 3rd thoracic segments large and obvious (Fig.
     16)—
                 case bearer:- Family GLOSSOSOMATIDAE (Genus GLOSSOSOMA)†

     † Consult the key by Wallace et al. (1990) to identify larvae in this Family.

—   Lateral plates on 2nd and 3rd thoracic segments small and
     inconspicuous (Figs 17–19)—   6

6   Basal membranous section of each anal proleg (Fig. 18, arrow a; Fig. 14,
     arrow) equal in length to distal sclerotized section. Undersides of femora
     with numerous long bristles (Fig. 18, arrow b)—
                 Family POLYCENTROPODIDAE (taxonomic notes, p. 57), 16

—   Anal prolegs have virtually no basal membranous section (Fig. 17,
     arrow a: Fig. 13, arrow). Undersides of femora with only a few isolated
     bristles (Fig. 17, arrow b)—
                 Family PSYCHOMYIIDAE (taxonomic notes, p. 63), 27

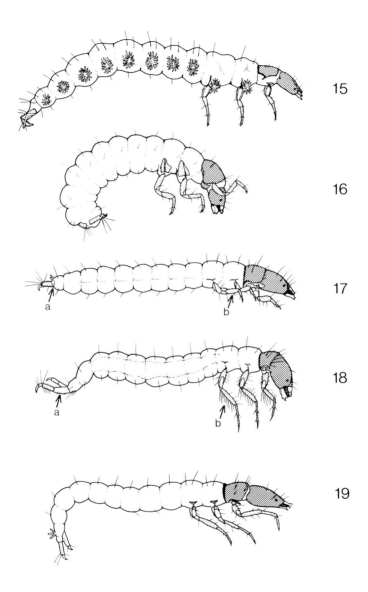

Figs 15–19. Typical larvae of various families. **15**, Rhyacophilidae. **16**, *Glossosoma* (Glossosomatidae). **17**, Psychomyiidae. **18**, Polycentropodidae. **19**, Philopotamidae.

7(2) Dorsal plates on 2nd and 3rd thoracic plates large and rectangular and similar in size to plates on 1st thoracic segment (Figs 22–24)—   **9**

— Dorsal plates on 2nd and 3rd thoracic segments much smaller than plates on 1st thoracic segment (Figs 20–21)—   **8**

8   1st leg much shorter than 2nd and 3rd legs (Fig. 20)—
                        case bearer:- Family BRACHYCENTRIDAE*

— 1st leg as long as 2nd and 3rd legs (Fig. 21)—
                        case bearer:- Family GLOSSOSOMATIDAE (Genus AGAPETUS)*

* Consult the key by Wallace et al. (1990) to identify larvae in these two Families.

9 (7) Tufted gills present on abdominal segments (Fig. 22); anal prolegs have terminal brush of long bristles (Fig. 22)—
                        Family HYDROPSYCHIDAE (taxonomic notes, p. 68), **38**

— No tufted gills on abdominal segments; anal prolegs without terminal brush (Figs 23, 24)—   **10**

10   Prominent lateral fringe of bristles on abdominal segments (Fig. 23)—
                        Family ECNOMIDAE
                        (taxonomic notes, p. 67) **Ecnomus tenellus** (Rambur)

— No lateral fringe of bristles on abdominal segments (Fig. 24)—
                        case bearer:- Family HYDROPTILIDAE (5th instar)†

† Consult the key by Wallace et al. (1990) to identify larvae in this Family.

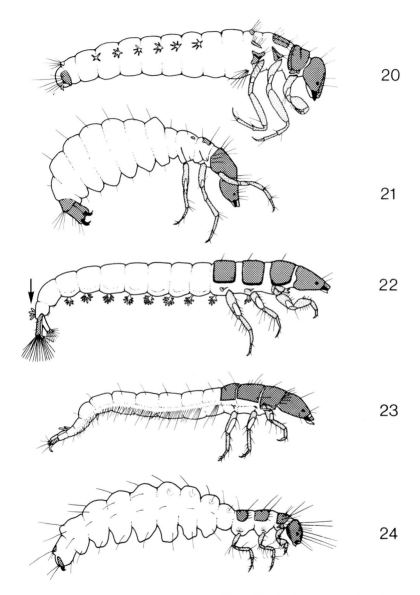

Figs 20–24. Typical larvae of various families. **20,** Brachycentridae. **21,** *Agapetus* (Glossosomatidae). **22,** Hydropsychidae (arrow points to the anal papillae). **23,** Ecnomidae. **24,** Hydroptilidae.

11 (3) Gills on 2nd and 3rd thoracic segments consist of a single filament (Fig. 25), those on abdominal segments with four filaments (Fig. 26). Auxiliary spine on anal prolegs, short (Fig. 28, arrow)—
Rhyacophila munda McLachlan

— Gills on thoracic and abdominal segments with numerous filaments (Fig. 27). Auxiliary spine on anal prolegs, long (Fig. 29, arrow)—   **12**

Figs 25–29. *Rhyacophila*. **25:** thoracic gill of *R. munda*. **26:** abdominal gills of *R. munda*. **27:** thoracic gills of *R. dorsalis*. **28–29:** anal claw and auxillary spine of:- 28, *R. munda*; 29, *R. septentrionis* (after Mackereth 1954).

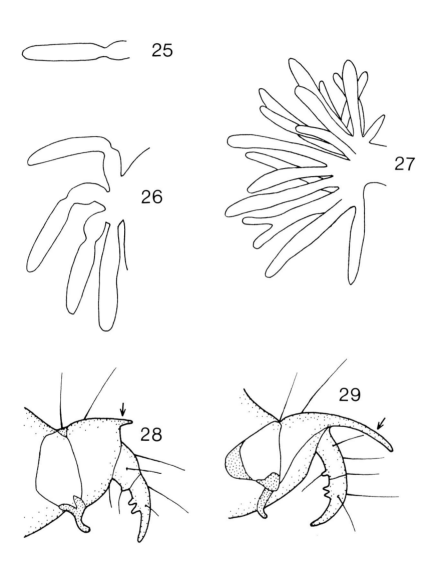

12 The table below compares characters for separating larvae of
Rhyacophila dorsalis, *R. obliterata* and *R. septentrionis*.

General pattern on the head:-	Posterior spots on the head:-	General pattern on the pronotum:-	Rear margin of the pronotum:-	Species:-
black transverse band (Fig. 30)	obscured (Fig. 30, arrow)	dark transverse band continuous (Fig. 31)	with brown areas (Fig. 31)	**Rhyacophila dorsalis** (Curtis)
brown transverse band (Fig. 32)	distinct (Fig. 32)	dark transverse band interrupted (Fig. 33)	entirely black (Fig. 33)	**Rhyacophila obliterata** McLachlan
dark-brown transverse band with lateral breaks (Fig. 34, arrows)	distinct (Fig. 34)	separate central and lateral dark areas (Fig. 35)	with brown areas (Fig. 35)	**Rhyacophila septentrionis** McLachlan

Figs 30–35. *Rhyacophila*. **30**: head capsule of *R. dorsalis*. **31**: pronotum of *R. dorsalis*. **32**: head capsule of *R. obliterata*. **33**: pronotum of *R. obliterata*. **34**: head capsule of *R. septentrionis*. **35**: pronotum of *R. septentrionis*.

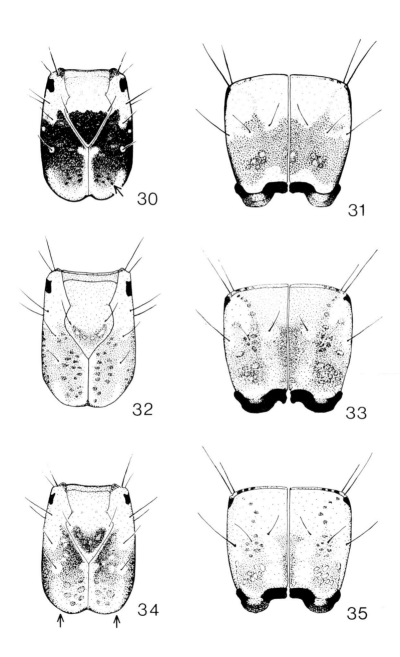

13 (4) Anterior margin of frontoclypeus has a smooth outline (Fig. 38)—
                                        Genus WORMALDIA, **15**

—   Anterior margin of frontoclypeus notched (Figs 36, 37)—   **14**

14   Notch in frontoclypeus deep and U-shaped (Fig. 36)—
                                        Chimarra marginata (L.)

—   Notch in frontoclypeus shallow and roughly V-shaped (Fig. 37)—
                                        Philopotamus montanus (Donovan)

15   Pronotum with marked posterior constriction and thick hind margin
     (Fig. 42, arrow c)—   **Wormaldia subnigra** McLachlan

—   Pronotum with slight posterior constriction and relatively thin hind
     margin (Fig. 41, arrow c)—   **Wormaldia occipitalis** (Pictet)

Figs 36–42. **36–38:** head capsule of:- 36, *Chimarra marginata*; 37, *Philopotamus montanus*; 38, *Wormaldia*. **39–42:** lateral views of pronotum and front coxa of philopotamid larvae (anterior to the right):- 39, *Chimarra marginata*; 40, *Philopotamus montanus*; 41, *Wormaldia occipitalis;* 42, *W. subnigra.*

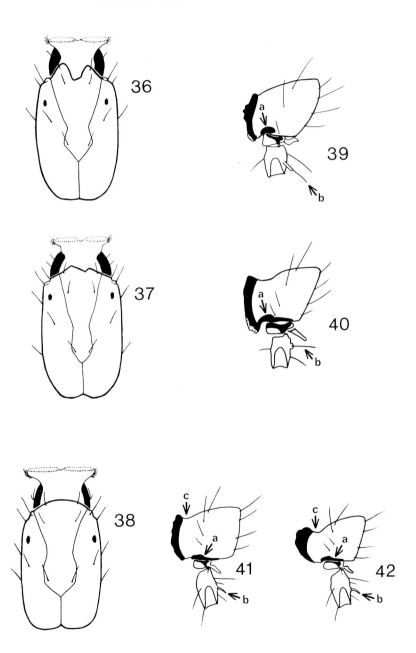

16 (6) Basal segment of anal prolegs without bristles (Fig. 43, arrows a). Ventral surface of 9th abdominal segment bears a pair of stout spines (Fig. 43, arrows b; Fig. 44)—   **Neureclipsis bimaculata** (L.)

— Basal segment of anal prolegs bears numerous bristles. 9th abdominal segment without stout ventral spines—   **17**

Figs 43–46. *Neureclipsis bimaculata*. **43**: anal prolegs (ventral view: a, basal segments; b, ventral spines). **44**: a ventral spine. **45**: anal claw (lateral view). **46**: head capsule.

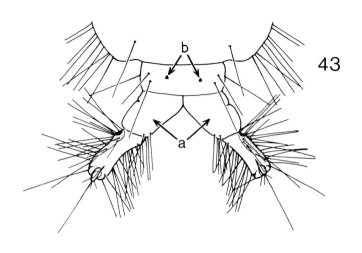

43

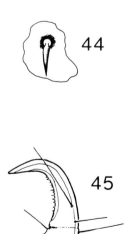

44

45

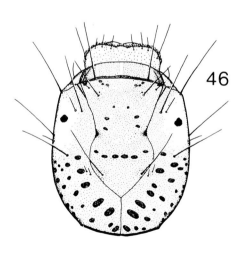

46

17   Anal claws with four blunt teeth on inside edge (Fig. 47)—
                                                   Genus CYRNUS, **18**

—   Anal claws without four blunt teeth on inside edge—   **20**

18   Dorsal surface of head with continuous dark bands (Fig. 48)—
                                                   Cyrnus trimaculatus (Curtis)

—   Dorsal surface of head without conspicuous dark bands (Figs 49, 50)—
                                                                       19

19   Central light area on the frontoclypeus includes some spots in the
     posterior row (Fig. 49)—   **Cyrnus flavidus** McLachlan

—   Central light area on the frontoclypeus does not include spots in the
     posterior row (Fig. 50)—   **Cyrnus insolutus** McLachlan

20 (17) Tarsus (Fig. 51, ta) of 1st leg less than half length of the tibia (Fig.
     51, ti)—   Genus POLYCENTROPUS, **21**

—   Tarsus of 1st leg about same length as the tibia (Fig. 52)—   **23**

Figs 47–52. **47**: anal claw (lateral view) of *Cyrnus*. **48–50**: head capsule of:- 48, *Cyrnus
trimaculatus*; 49, *C. flavidus*; 50, *C. insolutus*. **51–52**: tibia and tarsus of 1st leg of:-
51, *Polycentropus*; 52, *Plectrocnemia*.

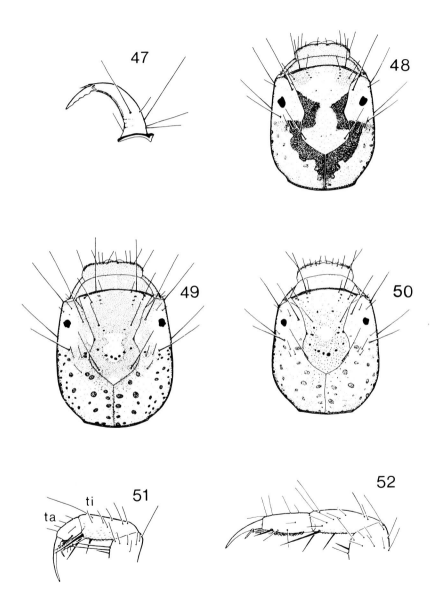

21 Dorsal surface of head without marked discontinuities of pigment (Fig.
    53)—   **Polycentropus irroratus** (Curtis)

—   Dorsal surface of head with marked discontinuities of pigment (Figs
    54–56)—   **22**

22 Anal claws obtuse-angled (Fig. 57)—
                                        Polycentropus kingi McLachlan

—   Anal claws right-angled (Fig. 58)—
                                Polycentropus flavomaculatus (Pictet)

23 (20) Anal claws obtuse-angled (Fig. 59)—   Genus PLECTROCNEMIA, **24**

—   Anal claws right-angled (Fig. 60)—   Genus HOLOCENTROPUS, **25**

Figs 53–58. *Polycentropus*. **53–56**: head capsule of:- 53, *P. irroratus;* 54, *P. kingi*; 55, 56,
    P. flavomaculatus. **57–58**: anal claw of:- 57, *P. kingi*; 58, *P. flavomaculatus*.

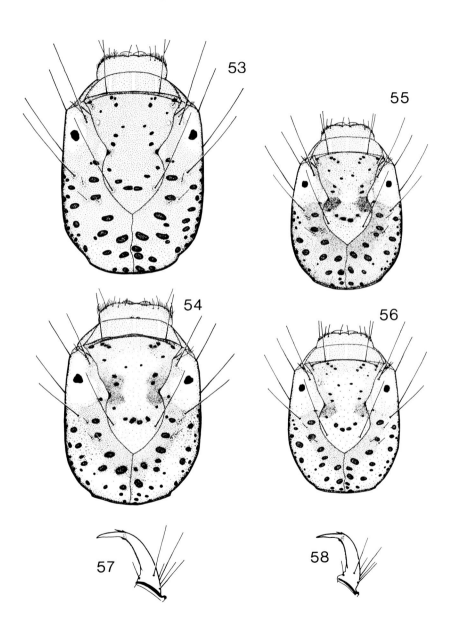

24   The table below compares characters for separating the larvae of *Plectrocnemia conspersa, P. brevis* and *P. geniculata*; (head capsules are illustrated on pp. 32–33).

Ventral; bristles on 9th abdominal segment:-	Posterior spots on frontoclypeus:-	Posterior mark on labrum:-	Dorsal secondary bristles on 9th abdominal segment (Fig. 69, ↗↗):-	Species
numerous (Fig. 61)	form a shallow arc (Fig. 63)	distinct (Fig. 66)	outer (Fig. 70, a) longer than inner (Fig. 70, b)	**Plectrocnemia conspersa** (Curtis)
numerous (Fig. 61)	form a V pattern (Fig. 64)	faint (Fig. 67)	outer and inner of similar length (Fig. 71)	**Plectrocnemia brevis** McLachlan
sparse (Fig. 62)	intermediate between other two species (Fig. 65)	absent (Fig. 68)	outer and inner of similar length (Fig. 72)	**Plectrocnemia geniculata** McLachlan

Figs 59–72. **59–60**: anal claw of:- 59, *Plectrocnemia*; 60, *Holocentropus*. **61–62**: 9th abdominal segment (ventral view) of:- 61, *P. conspersa* and *P. brevis*; 62, *P. geniculata*. **63–65**: posterior region of frontoclypeus of:- 63, *P. conspersa*; 64, *P. brevis*; 65, *P. geniculata*. **66–68**: labrum (dorsal view) of:- 66, *P. conspersa*; 67, *P. brevis*; 68, *P. geniculata*. **69**: 9th abdominal segment (dorsal view) of *Plectrocnemia*. **70–72**: dorsal bristles on 9th abdominal segment of:- 70, *P. conspersa*; 71, *P. brevis*; 72, *P. geniculata*, (modified from Wallace & Wallace 1983).

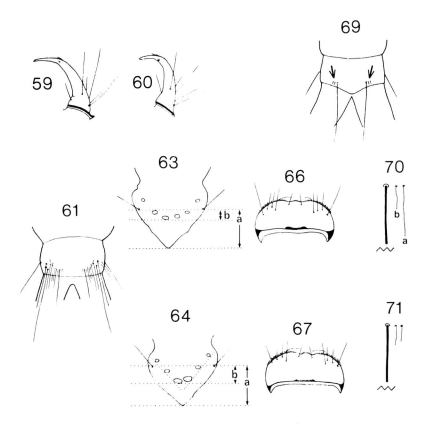

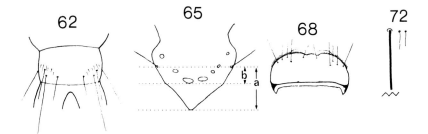

(24) Head capsules of *Plectrocnemia conspersa* (Figs 73, 74) and *P. geniculata* (Fig. 75) are illustrated here for general comparison with other genera in the key. The head markings of larvae in the genus *Plectrocnemia* exhibit considerable variation (see taxonomic notes, p. 61)

Figs 73–75. *Plectrocnemia*. Head capsule of:- **73, 74**, *P. conspersa*; **75**, *P. geniculata*.

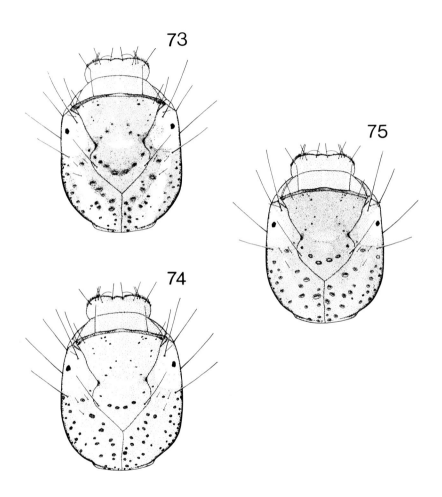

25 (23) Dorsal surface of head with dark bands of pigmentation and pale
median stripe on frontoclypeus (Figs 76, 77)—   **26**

—   Dorsal surface of head without distinct dark bands of pigmentation. No
continuous median stripe on frontoclypeus (Fig. 78)—
                                           Holocentropus dubius (Rambur)

26   Head broad and short. Pale median stripe on frontoclypeus clouded with
pigment at anterior end. No light areas alongside constriction of
frontoclypeus (Fig. 76)—   **Holocentropus stagnalis** (Albarda)

—   Head narrow and elongate. Pale median stripe on frontoclypeus clear of
pigment at its anterior end. Light areas present alongside constriction of
frontoclypeus (Fig. 77)—   **Holocentropus picicornis** (Stephens)

Figs 76–78. *Holocentropus*. Head capsule of:- **76**, *H. stagnalis*; **77**, *H. picicornis*; **78**, *H. dubius*.

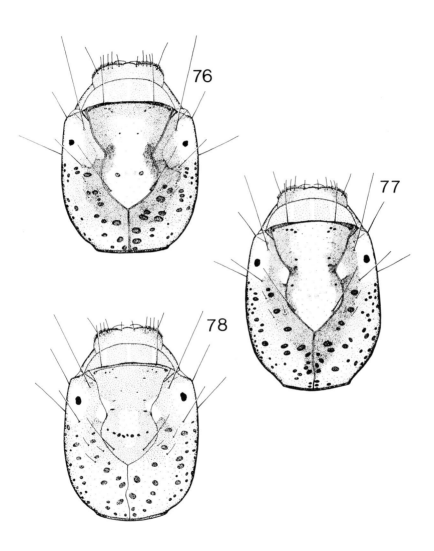

27 (6) Pronotum has black thickening in posterior-lateral position (Fig. 80, arrow)   **28**

—   Pronotum lacks black thickening in posterior-lateral position (Fig. 81)—
                                                                              29

28   Mentum black and heavily ornamented (Fig. 82)—
                                                     Psychomyia pusilla (Fabr.)

—   Mentum brown, smooth and not ornamented (Fig. 83)
                                                     Metalype fragilis (Pictet)

29 (27) Anterior part of coxopleurite* of 1st leg has two vertical black bars (Fig. 87, arrows)—   Genus TINODES, **31**

—   Anterior part of coxopleurite* of 1st leg has only one vertical black bar (Fig. 88, arrow)—   Genus LYPE, **30**

* The coxopleurites are small plates above the bases of the legs.

Figs 79–88. **79–81**: lateral view of head and prothorax of:- 79, *Ecnomus tenellus*; 80, *Psychomyia*; 81, *Tinodes*. **82–83**: head (ventral view) to show mentum of:- 82, *Psychomia pusilla*; 83, *Metalype fragilis*. **84–86**: anal claw of:- 84, *Psychomia pusilla*; 85, 86, *Metalype fragilis*. **87–88**: 1st coxopleurite (anterior to the right) of:- 87, *Tinodes*; 88, *Lype*.

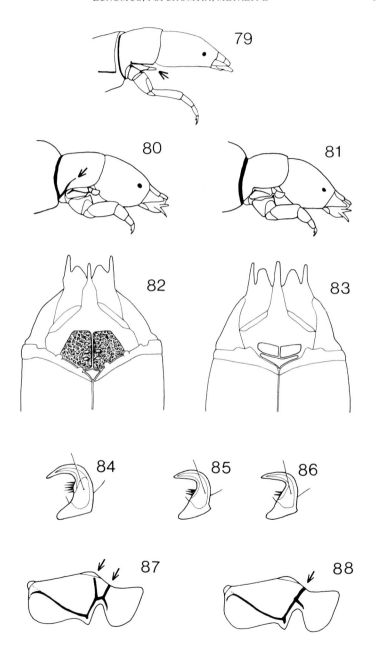

30   Frontoclypeus has two distinct colour zones; a pale anterior zone and a
     dark posterior zone which is continuous with the dark transverse band
     on the adjacent parts of the head (Fig. 89)—   **Lype reducta** (Hagen)

—   Frontoclypeus relatively uniform in colour without clearly defined
     anterior and posterior zones (Fig. 90)—   **Lype phaeopa** (Stephens)

31 (29) Pronotum has large ovoid yellow marks on either side of mid-line
     (Fig. 94); frontoclypeus conspicuously darker than adjacent areas of the
     head (Fig. 95)—   **Tinodes waeneri** (L.)

—   Pronotum without ovoid yellow marks; frontoclypeus not markedly
     different in pigment intensity from adjacent areas of the head (Figs 99,
     100, 105–107)—   **32**

Figs 89–95. **89–92**: head capsules of *Lype*:- 89, *L. reducta* (dorsal view); 90, *L. phaeopa* (dorsal
     view); 91, *L. reducta* (ventral view); 92, *L. phaeopa* (ventral view). **93–95**: *Tinodes
     waeneri*:- 93, anal claw; 94, pronotum (dorsal view); 95, head capsule (dorsal view).

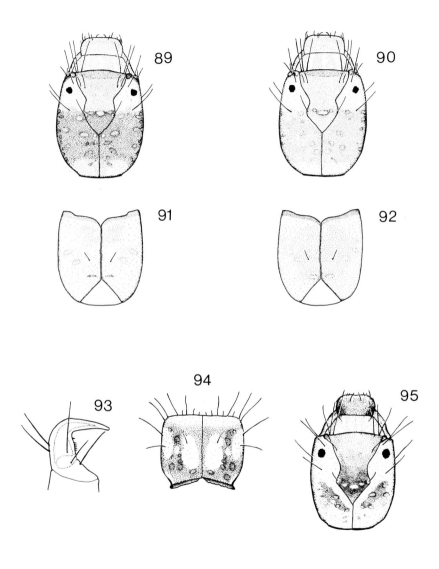

32   Labrum uniformly pale (Fig. 96)—   **Tinodes unicolor** (Pictet)

—   Labrum with dark pigmentation either evenly or unevenly distributed
     (Figs 97, 98)—   **33**

33   Labrum uniformly black or dark brown except for pale anterior margin
     (Fig. 97)—   **34**

—   Labrum pigmentation of uneven intensity and with greatest
     concentration around posterior-lateral points (Fig. 98)—   **35**

34   Coxopleurites of 2nd and 3rd legs lightly pigmented (Fig. 101). Of the
     two vertical arms on the coxopleurite of the 1st leg, the posterior arm is
     long, and sharply defined (Fig. 103, arrow)—
                                              Tinodes rostocki McLachlan

—   Coxopleurites of 2nd and 3rd legs heavily pigmented (Fig. 102). Of the
     two vertical black arms on the coxopleurite of the 1st leg, the posterior
     arm is short and ends in diffuse pigmentation (Fig. 104, arrow)—
                                                   Tinodes dives (Pictet)

Figs 96–104.   *Tinodes*. **96–98**: labrum of:- 96, *T. unicolor*; 97, *T. dives*; 98, *T. assimilis*. **99–100**:
            head capsule of:- 99, *T. dives*; 100, *T. unicolor*. **101–102**: 2nd coxopleurite
            (anterior to the right; head of coxa shown by dotted line) of:- 101, *T. rostocki*;
            102, *T. dives*. **103**: 1st coxopleurite of *T. dives* (anterior to the right).

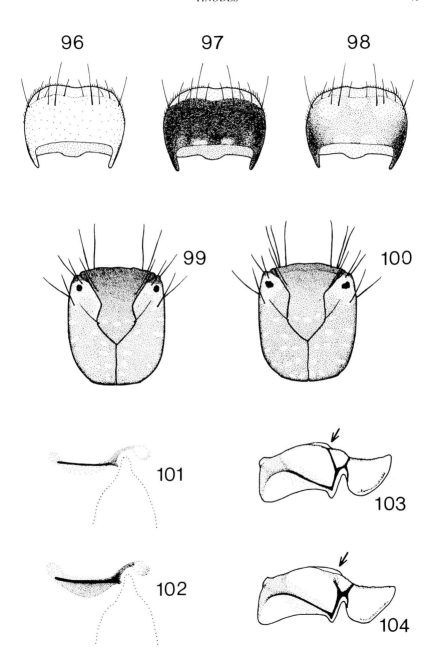

35 (33) Frontoclypeus has single dominant pale spot in posterior region;
other spots on frontoclypeus and rest of dorsal head surface indistinct
(Fig. 107)—   **Tinodes pallidulus** McLachlan

—   Frontoclypeus has three similar pale spots in posterior region; spots on
frontoclypeus and rest of dorsal head surface distinct (Figs 105, 106)—
36

36 Reddish-purple pigment patch present on underside of 2nd thoracic
segment (Fig. 108, arrow)—   **37**

—   No pigment patch on underside of 2nd thoracic segment—
Tinodes maculicornis (Pictet)

37 Dorsal surface of each anal proleg has a series of 3–5 pale spots (Fig.
109). On the coxopleurite of the 1st leg, the trochantin (i.e. the anterior
leaf-like structure) is appreciably darker in colour than the posterior-
ventral area (Fig. 111, arrows)—   **Tinodes assimilis** McLachlan

—   Dorsal surface of each anal proleg has only a single distinct pale spot
(Fig. 110). On the coxopleurite of the 1st leg, the trochantin is similar in
colour to the posterior-ventral area (Fig. 112, arrows)—
Tinodes maclachlani (Kimmins)

Figs 105–112. *Tinodes*. **105–107**: head capsule of:- 105, *T. assimilis*; 106, *T. maclachlani*; 107,
T. pallidulus. **108**: underside of 2nd thoracic segment of *T. maclachlani*, with
pigment patch. **109–110**: anal prolegs (dorsal view) of:- 109, *T. assimilis*; 110, *T.
maclachlani*. **111–112**: 1st coxopleurite (lateral view; anterior to the right) of:-
111, *T. assimilis*; 112, *T. maclachlani*.

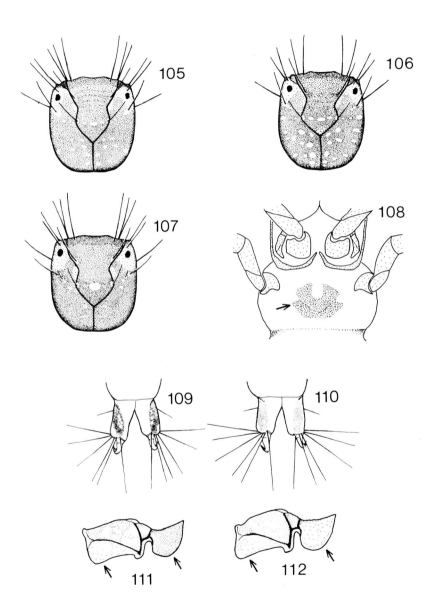

38 (9) Front margin of pronotum has numerous long bristles (Fig. 113)—
                                    Cheumatopsyche lepida (Pictet)

— Front margin of pronotum without numerous long bristles (Fig. 114)—
                                                                      39

39 Dorsal head surface uniformly brown in colour without yellow markings
    (Fig. 115). Dorsal plates on 2nd and 3rd thoracic segments with
    transverse sutures (Fig. 117, arrows)—   **Diplectrona felix** McLachlan

— Dorsal head surface with conspicuous yellow markings (e.g. Figs 121,
    130–134). Dorsal plates on 2nd and 3rd thoracic segments without
    transverse sutures (Fig. 118)—   **40**

Figs 113–118. **113–114**: head and pronotum (lateral view) of:- 113, *Cheumatopsyche lepida*;
        114, *Hydropsyche* (arrow indicates trochantin). **115**: head capsule of *Diplectrona*
        felix. **116**: head and pronotum (lateral view) of *D. felix* (arrow indicates
        trochantin). **117–118**: 1st, 2nd and 3rd thoracic plates (dorsal view) of:- 117, *D.*
        felix (arrows indicate·transverse sutures); 118, *Hydropsyche*.

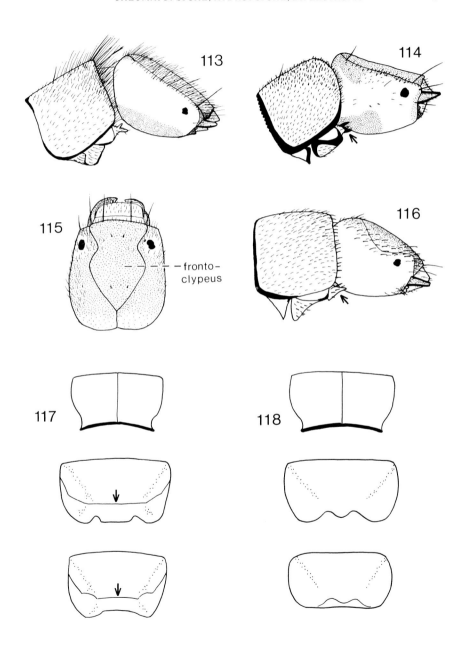

113

114

115

116

fronto-
clypeus

117

118

40   Gills absent on 7th abdominal segment (Fig. 119)—
                                   Hydropsyche siltalai Döhler

—   Gills present on 7th abdominal segment (Fig. 120)—   **41**

41   Posterior prosternites (on underside of 1st thoracic segment) entirely
     pale (Fig. 124, arrows)—   **42**

—   Posterior prosternites partly pigmented (Fig. 122, arrows) or entirely
     dark (Fig. 141)—   **43**

Figs 119–124. **119–120**: posterior of abdomen (lateral view) of:- 119, *Hydropsyche siltalai*; 120, *Hydropsyche* species other than *H. siltalai*. **121**: head capsule of *H. siltalai* **122–124**: underside of 1st thoracic segments to show the posterior prosternites (arrowed):- 122, typical condition in *Hydropsyche* species; 123, *Cheumatopsyche lepida*; 124, *Hydropsyche contubernalis* and *H. bulgaromanorum*.

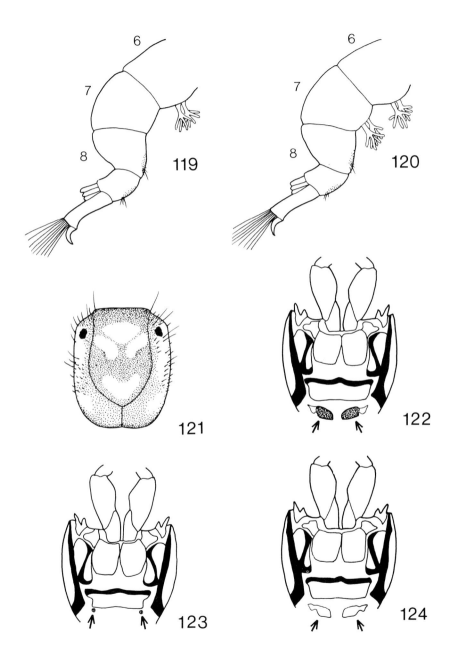

42   Submentum (position shown in Fig. 125) has conspicuous central knob
     (Fig. 126). Frontoclypeus is largely obscured by mat of long setae (Fig.
     128)—   **Hydropsyche bulgaromanorum** Malicky

—   Submentum lacks central knob (Fig. 127). Frontoclypeus not obscured
     by mat of setae, pattern clearly visible (Figs 130, 131)—
                                   Hydropsyche contubernalis McLachlan

Figs 125–131. *Hydropsyche*. **125**: ventral view of head to show position of submentum.
126–127: submentum of:- 126, *H. bulgaromanorum*; 127, *H. contubernalis*.
128–131: head capsule of:- 128, *H. bulgaromanorum*, covered with setae and
debris; 129, *H. bulgaromanorum*, cleaned head capsule; 130, 131, *H.
contubernalis*. (On the figures, species are indicated by initial letters: b and c).

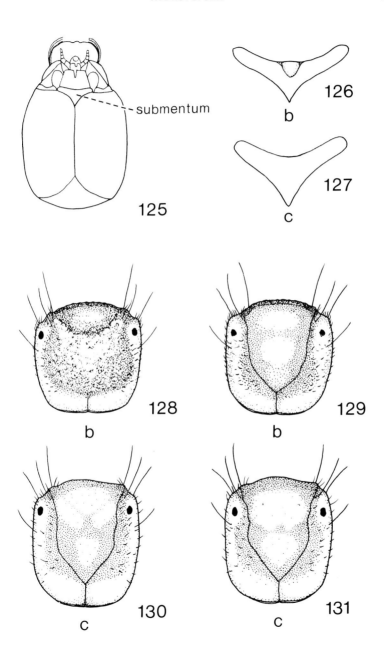

submentum

125

126
b

127
c

128
b

129
b

130
c

131
c

43 (41) Frontoclypeal pattern with aboral and lateral marks separated (Figs
         132–134)—   **44**

—   Frontoclypeal pattern with aboral and lateral marks joined to form a
         continuous sinuate figure (Figs 144–145)—   **46**

44   Prosternites with both medial and lateral sections darkly pigmented (Fig.
         141)—   **Hydropsyche angustipennis** (Curtis)

—   Prosternites bicoloured, with medial sections distinctly darker than
         lateral sections (Figs 142, 143)—   **45**

45   Frontoclypeus with aboral mark in the shape of a Y or bar-shaped (Fig.
         133), frontoclypeus V-shaped in outline—
                                                   Hydropsyche pellucidula (Curtis)

—   Frontoclypeus with aboral mark in the shape of a U or a V (Fig. 134),
         frontoclypeus U-shaped in outline—   **Hydropsyche instabilis** (Curtis)

Figs 132–143. *Hydropsyche*. **132-134**: head capsule (dorsal view) of:- 132, *H. angustipennis*;
    133, *H. pellucidula*; 134, *H. instabilis*. **135–137**: head capsule (ventral view) of:-
    135, *H. angustipennis* (arrow indicates median suture); 136, *H. pellucidula*; 137,
    H. instabilis. **138–140**: submentum of:- 138, *H. angustipennis*; 139, *H.
    pellucidula*; 140, *H. instabilis*. **141–143**: posterior prosternite of:- 141, *H.
    angustipennis*; 142, *H. pellucidula*; 143, *H. instabilis*. (On the figures, species are
    indicated by initial letters: a, i and p).

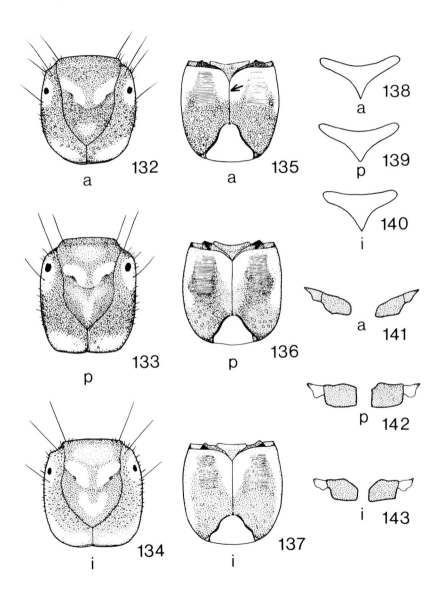

132 a

135 a

138 a

139 p

140 i

133 p

136 p

141 a

134 i

137 i

142 p

143 i

46 (43) Posterior margin of frontoclypeus and adjacent areas of head with pustular (nodular) ornamentation (Fig. 144)—
Hydropsyche exocellata Dufour

— Posterior margin of frontoclypeus and adjacent areas of head without pustular ornamentation (Figs 145, 146)—   **47**

47 Ventral surface of head has pale transverse anterior band with a pale median extension (Fig. 148)—   **Hydropsyche fulvipes** (Curtis)

— Ventral side of head has neither pale anterior band nor pale median extension (Fig. 149)—   **Hydropsyche saxonica** McLachlan

Figs 144–155. *Hydropsyche*. **144–146**: head capsule (dorsal view) of:- 144, *H. exocellata*; 145, *H. fulvipes*; 146, *H. saxonica*. **147–149**: head capsule (ventral view) of:- 147, *H. exocellata*; 148, *H. fulvipes*; 149, *H. saxonica*. **150–152**: submentum of:- 150, *H. exocellata*; 151, *H. fulvipes*; 152, *H. saxonica*. **153–155**: posterior prosternites of:- 153, *H. exocellata*; 154, *H. fulvipes*; 155, *H. saxonica*.
(On the figures, species are indicated by initial letters: e, f and s).

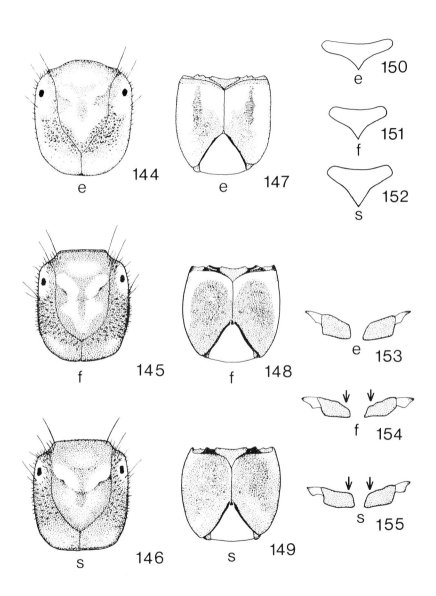

TAXONOMIC NOTES

RHYACOPHILIDAE

Rhyacophila·munda

This species is readily distinguished from the others by the arrangement of gills and the structure of the anal prolegs (Figs 25–29). Larvae from Spain have been fully described by Viedma & Jalón (1980) who comment on the variability in head markings and on the fact that the head is markedly constricted at the level of the eyes, a point also made by Mackereth (1954). Little is known about the habitat distribution of this species except that it has been found in both small streams and medium-sized rivers (Mackereth 1954; Jenkins 1979).

Rhyacophila dorsalis, R. obliterata and *R. septentrionis*

The separation of these three species is complicated by the considerable variation in markings within each of them and users of the original version of our key have expressed reservations about its practicability. We have, therefore, examined again the various characters suggested by Mackereth (1954), Hickin (1954) and Lepneva (1970) and reviewed them in the light of recent observations made by Pitsch (1993).

We conclude that pigmentation features on the dorsal surfaces of the head and pronotum provide the best means of separation but that it is best to review the range of characters in each case rather than give priority to particular ones. For this reason we offer a table at this point in the key (on p. 20), rather than paired couplets.

Head markings of *Rhyacophila*

Head pigmentation in *R. dorsalis* is usually darker than in other species, with a sharp contrast between the cream-coloured anterior band and the region behind it which is largely black (Fig. 30). This dark pigmentation typically obscures the spots of muscle insertions (Fig. 30, arrow) on either side of the coronal suture.

In *R. septentrionis* the head pigmentation is very variable but, in lightly pigmented individuals, two longitudinal pale bands separating the lateral and the central pigment areas are apparent (Fig. 34, arrows). In all cases the posterior spots of muscle insertions are much more conspicuous than in *dorsalis*.

R. obliterata is more diffusely pigmented than the other two species (Fig. 32). The mark in the apex of the frontoclypeus is faint and takes the form of a shallow U rather than a heart-shape (which is the condition in *dorsalis*). The spots alongside the coronal suture are more clearly visible than in *dorsalis*. Larvae of *obliterata* are appreciably larger than larvae of the other species, with the final instar head-widths reaching 1.6 mm compared with a maximum of 1.45 mm for the other species. They also have a more markedly concave anterior margin of the frontoclypeus.

Pronotum markings of *Rhyacophila*

With respect to this character, the three species seem to form a series with decreasing pigmentation. In *dorsalis* the transverse mark on the pronotum is continuous (Fig. 31), in *obliterata* it is partly interrupted by pale spots (Fig. 33) and in *septentrionis* the longitudinal spots normally merge to produce a clear separation between the lateral pigment masses and the median vase-shaped pigment area (Fig. 35).

Pronotum posterior margin of *Rhyacophila*

To view this character it is usually necessary to push back the overlapping lobe of the 2nd thoracic segment or to detach the head together with the 1st thoracic segment from the rest of the body. In *obliterata* the posterior margin of the pronotum forms a continuous thick jet-black band (interrupted only by the median suture) (Fig. 33). In *septentrionis* and *dorsalis* this band is lighter in the region of the backward-projecting lobes. In *septentrionis* this results in a sector which is dark brown rather than black (Fig. 35) and in *dorsalis* the sector is brown or even yellow (Fig. 31). In *dorsalis* the light crescent in the front part of the lobe is usually bounded by a thin but distinct black pigment line.

Of these three *Rhyacophila* species in Britain, *dorsalis* appears to be the most widespread, closely followed by *obliterata*. *R. septentrionis* appears to be more localised and an association with calcareous streams, reported by

Hickin (1954) and Mackereth (1954), also applied to our collecting sites in South Wales.
Records collected by Pitsch (1993) from Central Europe suggest that *septentrionis* extends further up into headwaters and *dorsalis* extends further downstream into larger rivers than does *obliterata*, but otherwise there is considerable overlap in distribution.

Rhyacophila larvae are free-moving predators and can be found in virtually any clean stream or river. They are usually encountered crawling closely pressed to rock surfaces in fast-flow conditions. The presence of *Rhyacophila* is also revealed by its characteristic pupal case. This is a bulky, gravel structure firmly fixed to a stone and containing a distinctive leathery, brown cocoon. Refer to pages 93, 105 and 118, respectively, for further details on the diet, habitat, and life cycles of rhyacophilid larvae.

PHILOPOTAMIDAE

The shape of the anterior margin of the frontoclypeus provides a simple means of separating the three genera in the family. When examining this character it may be necessary to push the membranous labrum forward to prevent it from obscuring the anterior margin. Similarly, if the mandibles have become reflected inwards care must be taken not to confuse their outline with that of the frontoclypeus.

In addition to this feature, the three genera can be separated by examining the pigmentation pattern on the side of the pronotum, and the structures on the anterior face of the front coxa.

In *Chimarra marginata* the black pigment on the pronotum is in the form of an ovoid spot (Fig. 39, arrow a) and the front coxa has a long process surmounted by a black bristle (Fig. 39, arrow b).

In *Philopotamus montanus* the black pigment is in the form of a band which is continuous with the black band on the rear of the pronotum (Fig. 40, arrow a) and the front coxa has a rounded protruberance bearing a black bristle (Fig. 40, arrow b).

In the *Wormaldia* species the black pigment is in the shape of an "eyebrow" (Fig. 41; Fig. 42, arrow a) and the anterior face of the front coxa carries a pale-coloured, thickened, curved spine (Fig. 41; Fig. 42, arrow b).

We have looked again at the various proposals for characters to separate *W. subnigra* from *W. occipitalis* and have also taken account of observations by Pitsch (1993) on European material. We conclude that the best distinguishing features are the greater degree of constriction of the rear part of the pronotum and the thicker posterior black band in *subnigra* (Fig. 42, arrow c). In *occipitalis* the constriction is much less marked and the posterior band much thinner relative to the overall size of the pronotum (Fig. 41, arrow c).

This still leaves unresolved the question of the third *Wormaldia* species, *mediana*. This species was reinstated in the British list by Kimmins (1953). Moretti (1983) considers that the larvae of *mediana* closely resemble those of *subnigra*. If this is the case, association with adults will be needed to confirm identifications of both *subnigra* and *mediana* larvae.

Philopotamus montanus and *Wormaldia* larvae are common in the rapids of small, fast-flowing streams, *W. occipitalis* being more widely distributed than either *W. subnigra* or *W. mediana* (Kimmins 1965). Compared with these species, *Chimarra marginata* appears to extend into larger streams.

Philopotamid larvae spin nets in the form of long tubular bags (Fig. 166) which are used to filter out small-sized food particles (p. 87).

POLYCENTROPODIDAE

Neureclipsis bimaculata

This species differs from all the other polycentropodid larvae in having a pair of stout spines on the ventral side of the 9th abdominal segment (Fig. 43, arrows b; Fig. 44) and in the absence of bristles on the basal segment of the anal prolegs (Fig. 43, arrows a).

Additional distinguishing features for *Neureclipsis* are the straight line of spots on the posterior part of the frontoclypeus (Fig. 46) and the numerous small spines on the inside edge of the anal claw (Fig. 45). These various characters are useful in 3rd to 5th instar larvae. In smaller larvae the ventral spines on the 9th abdominal segment are longer and extend to the base of the anal prolegs.

A useful feature for distinguishing early instar *Neureclipsis* larvae is that the setae on the lower margin of the front femur are uniformly long. In other species they vary in length (H. Tachet, pers. comm.).

Unlike most polycentropodid nets, which are very variable in form, *Neureclipsis* nets are sufficiently distinctive to assist in species recognition. They are invariably trumpet-shaped with a narrow tail looping forward

(Fig. 162). *Neureclipsis* is localised in its distribution in Britain and is usually found in lake outflow streams. See pages 78, 96 and 111, respectively, for further notes on the net and diet, habitat, and life cycles.

Genus CYRNUS

Cyrnus larvae always have four blunt teeth on the inside margin of the anal claw (Fig. 47). This is a reliable character even for early instar larvae and should be easily detectable with a binocular microscope using x50 magnification.

C. trimaculatus is the most distinctive of the three species, with dark bands of pigment on the dorsal side of the head (Fig. 48). In *C. flavidus* and *C. insolutus* the patterns are muted and the important difference between them is that in *flavidus* some of the dark posterior spots on the frontoclypeus fall within the central light area, whereas this is not the case with *insolutus* (Figs 49, 50). Other features of the head pattern are not sufficiently consistent to be used for identification.

C. trimaculatus is the commonest species and is widely distributed in ponds, lakes and slow-flowing rivers. *C. flavidus* has a similar habitat distribution but occurs less frequently in rivers. *C. insolutus* is rare in Britain and to date is known only from Blelham Tarn in the English Lake District (Kimmins 1942; Edington 1964) and from a pond known as the Oval Pond, near Mortimer in Berkshire (H. Malicky, pers. comm.). Adults and larvae have been collected in Ireland from Lough Derrygeeha in County Clare (O'Connor 1977).

Cyrnus larvae sometimes construct distinctive food-catching nets on aquatic plants (Fig. 163), but more often the nets are found under stones as irregular masses of threads (p. 78).

Genus POLYCENTROPUS

Later instar larvae of *Polycentropus* are distinguishable from the remaining genera in the key (*Plectrocnemia* and *Holocentropus*) by the shortness of the prothoracic tarsi relative to the tibiae (Fig. 51). Indeed, the tarsal segment is so short in *Polycentropus* that there is a risk of mistaking it for part of the claw, especially if the leg is flexed. It is important when examining this character to ensure that it is the tibia and tarsus which are being compared and not the tarsus and the femur. The size distinction between the tibia and tarsus is less obvious with smaller larvae and the segments are of equal length in the 1st instar. In *Polycentropus flavomaculatus*, for example, the ratio of tibia to tarsus changes as follows: 1st instar 1 : 1, 2nd instar 1.25 : 1, 3rd instar 1.5 : 1, 4th instar 1.8 : 1, 5th instar 2.4 : 1.

Among the three *Polycentropus* species, *irroratus* is differentiated by having a head with a fairly uniform background colour against which the spots stand out very clearly (Fig. 53). In both *flavomaculatus* and *kingi* the head is distinctly banded and this is apparent even to the naked eye (Figs 54–56). Some difficulties may be encountered in separating these latter two species. *P. kingi* is best distinguished by having an obtuse-angled anal claw (Fig. 57), unlike *P. flavomaculatus* where the claw is right-angled (Fig. 58). In making this judgement it is important to view the side face of the claw at right-angles, if necessary by examining it flat on a microscope slide.

In the material we have examined there are also fairly subtle differences in head markings, involving the relative positions of spots and pigment areas on the frontoclypeus. Each species has an arc of spots on the posterior part of the frontoclypeus, consisting typically of four large spots with two smaller and separate lateral spots. In *flavomaculatus* (Figs 55, 56) these lateral spots are usually contained within the darkly-pigmented area, whereas in *kingi* (Fig. 54) they generally lie posterior to it.

P. flavomaculatus is the typical polycentropodid of the lower reaches of rivers, but is also abundant in small rivers and streams that are sufficiently productive; it is also common on stony lake shores and can often be found, alongside *Neureclipsis*, in lake outflows. *P. kingi* and *irroratus* are rarer and typically appear in small numbers in river samples dominated by *flavomaculatus*. The form of the food-catching nets of *Polycentropus* is rarely apparent because they are usually built underneath stones and collapse into a mass of silk when the stone is overturned. See pages 76, 96 and 108 for further descriptions of the biology of *Polycentropus*.

Genus PLECTROCNEMIA

Plectrocnemia larvae resemble *Holocentropus* larvae in having prothoracic tibiae and tarsi of approximately equal length, but differ from them in that *Plectrocnemia* has obtuse-angled claws (Fig. 59) whereas *Holocentropus* has right-angled claws (Fig. 60).

Since the previous edition of this key, Wallace & Wallace (1983) have found the previously unknown larvae of *Plectrocnemia brevis* McLachlan, and have been able to describe characters for separating the three British species in the genus. These characters relate to the arrangement of bristles on the last abdominal segment, the pattern of spots at the apex of the frontoclypeus, and the pigmentation of the labrum. As there is considerable variation in some of these characters, a tabular arrangement has been adopted for the key at this point (p. 30) to allow the various characters to be considered simultaneously.

Bristles on the last abdominal segment of *Plectrocnemia*

In all three *Plectrocnemia* species the ventral surface of the last abdominal segment bears eight (4 pairs) long primary bristles. Smaller, secondary bristles are also present and it is the arrangement of these which provides useful distinguishing features between the species (Wallace & Wallace 1983). In *conspersa* and *brevis* these secondary bristles are numerous (9 to 57 on 5th instar larvae and 6 to 21 on 4th instar larvae) and mostly long (Fig. 61). By contrast, in *geniculata* they are sparse and short (4 to 14 in number on 5th instar larvae and 1 to 5 on 4th instar larvae) (Fig. 62). It needs to be remembered that bristles can break off, reducing the apparent number, although when this happens the bristle sockets may still be apparent. We have occasionally found larvae of *conspersa* where the secondary bristles are virtually absent on one half of the segment but normal on the other.

The secondary bristles on the dorsal side of the last abdominal segment provide a distinguishing feature for *conspersa*. These secondary bristles are situated lateral to the large primary bristles on either side of the mid-line (Fig. 69, arrows). In *conspersa* the outer bristle in this pair is at least twice the length of the inner one in the 5th instar (Fig. 70) and about one and a half times as long as in the 4th instar. By contrast, in both *brevis* and *geniculata* the secondary bristles are of approximately equal length (Figs 71, 72). Inevitably, however, in some specimens these small bristles will have become detached.

Head markings of *Plectrocnemia*

Wallace & Wallace (1983) draw attention to differences between the species in the positioning of the posterior spots on the frontoclypeus. In *conspersa* the spots form a shallow arc (Fig. 63), in *brevis* they are arranged in a V shape (at least in the 5th instar larvae) (Fig. 64), and in *geniculata* their arrangement is intermediate between the two (Fig. 65). These differences can be quantified by expressing them in terms of the ratio a/b (Figs 63, 65). In *conspersa*, values for the ratio are 3.2 to 14.8 in the 5th instar and 5.4 to 29.0 in the 4th instar. In *brevis*, values for the ratio are 1.7 to 3.0 in the 5th instar and 3.0 to 4.5 in the 4th instar, and in *geniculata* they are 2.2 to 3.4 in the 5th instar and 3.3 to 4.3 in the 4th instar. A microscope with a micrometer eyepiece will be required for making the necessary measurements to calculate the ratios.

The pigmentation along the posterior margin of the labrum also differs in the three species. To examine this feature it is usually necessary to draw out the labrum from the plate (the anteclypeus) overlying it. It is reliable only for final instar larvae. In *conspersa* an elongated pigment patch is present in a median position (Fig. 66). In *brevis* the patch is usually present (Fig. 67) although less distinct than in *conspersa*. In *geniculata* it is absent, although two widely separated indistinct spots may be detectable along the rear margin (Fig. 68).

Head markings in *Plectrocnemia* larvae vary considerably, with *conspersa* showing a particularly wide range, extending all the way from individuals with contrasting light and dark banding (Fig. 73) to those where the background colour is a fairly uniform dull-yellow (Fig. 74). These pale individuals conceivably could be confused with *Polycentropus irroratus* (Fig. 53). However, even without the difference in segment lengths of the forelegs (Figs 51, 52), *Plectrocnemia* has a much squarer and less-elongated head shape (Figs 73–75) than *P. irroratus* (Fig. 53).

Plectrocnemia conspersa is the common polycentropodid in the upper reaches of river systems, being particularly abundant in acidic or metal-polluted streams (see pp. 94–96). It also occurs in some upland pools and lakes. *P. geniculata* is less common but overlaps in distribution with *conspersa*, although in Central Europe it does not extend as far downstream, according to Pitsch (1993). Wallace & Wallace (1983) have found *P. brevis* in the counties of Devon, Cheshire, Clwyd and Merseyside and suggest that it may be particularly associated with calcareous streams.

Plectrocnemia nets are often very conspicuous objects on the beds of small streams, the form of the net varying with water depth and flow rate (Figs 156–160 and p. 76).

Genus HOLOCENTROPUS

Holocentropus larvae are considerably smaller, instar for instar, than *Plectrocnemia* and differ in having right-angled (Fig. 60) rather than obtuse-angled (Fig. 59) anal claws. Head-widths in 5th instar *Holocentropus* range from 1.20 to 1.60 mm, compared with 1.85 to 2.70 mm in *Plectrocnemia*.

There is usually no difficulty in separating the three *Holocentropus* species from one another on the basis of head markings and head shape. *H. dubius* has a superficial resemblance to *Cyrnus flavidus* but can be distinguished by having pale areas inside and outside the frontoclypeus at the point of constriction (Fig. 78); *C. flavidus* has only the outside marks (Fig. 49). *Cyrnus* larvae should in any case have been intercepted at couplet 17 of the key on the basis of their toothed anal claws.

Where *H. picicornis* and *H. dubius* live together in the same site, their life cycles may be staggered, with the result that throughout the winter *dubius* larvae are the larger of the two (pp. 110–111).

Holocentropus larvae occur in the still waters of lakes, ponds and canals. *H. stagnalis* seems to be more local in its distribution than the other two species. *Holocentropus* nets take the form of plate-like or funnel-shaped structures attached to aquatic vegetation (p. 78; Fig. 161).

PSYCHOMYIIDAE

Psychomyia pusilla and *Metalype fragilis*

These two species are readily distinguishable from other psychomyiids by the diagonal black thickening on the posterior-lateral margin of the pronotum (Fig. 80, arrow). They can be separated from each other on the form of the ventral head sclerites. In *Psychomyia pusilla* the anterior paired sclerites (forming the mentum) are black and heavily ornamented, with each plate as long as it is broad (Fig. 82). The corresponding plates in *Metalype fragilis* are brown and smooth, lacking ornamentation, and each plate is only about half as long as it is broad (Fig. 83). The single plate behind the mentum (i.e. the submentum) also differs in the two species; in *P. pusilla* it is in the form of a small regular triangle (Fig. 82), whereas in *M. fragilis* it is considerably expanded laterally (Fig. 83). There are also differences in the number of spines on the anal claws. In *P. pusilla* there are 5 or 6 spines (Fig. 84) and in *M. fragilis* there are 2 or 3 spines (Figs 85, 86). These various characters allow the separation of the larvae in the 3rd, 4th and 5th (final) instars.

P. pusilla larvae grow slowly in the winter (Fig. 185), so when they occur at the same site as a faster-growing species, such as *Tinodes dives* (Fig. 183), there can be a marked difference in size between the two species in the early part of the year.

P. pusilla is common in large streams and rivers (Alderson 1969; Jenkins 1977; Cooling 1982). *M. fragilis* is more localised and records to date suggest there is an association with calcareous streams and lakes (Edington & Alderson 1973; Cooling 1982).

Genus LYPE

Lype larvae differ from *Tinodes* larvae in having one bar (Fig. 88, arrow) rather than two vertical bars (Fig. 87, arrows) on the first coxopleurite.

The separation of *Lype reducta* and *L. phaeopa* presents some difficulty. In our material the band of pigment across the dorsal side of the head is darker in *reducta* and consequently divides the frontoclypeus into posterior dark and anterior light zones (Fig. 89). No such clear division is apparent in the *phaeopa* we have examined and in most specimens the frontoclypeus is virtually uniform in colour (Fig. 90). In addition, the spots on the ventral surface of the head are usually more distinct in *reducta* (Fig. 91) than in *phaeopa* (Fig. 92). These distinguishing features must, however, be regarded as provisional until the two species become more widely known.

Lype constructs galleries on submerged branches in streams, rivers, ponds and lakes. The walls of the galleries consist of wood fragments and sand grains held together with silk. Although there has been a tendency to regard *L. reducta* as the rarer of the two species (Hickin 1967), both appear to be common in South Wales (Edington & Alderson 1973; Jenkins 1977).

Genus TINODES

Tinodes waeneri

Mature larvae of *T. waeneri* are easily separated from the other *Tinodes* larvae by the distinctive markings on the head and pronotum which are apparent even to the naked eye (Figs 95, 94). These markings are clear in 5th instar larvae, sometimes apparent in 4th and 3rd, but absent in 2nd and 1st instars. However, all *T. waeneri* larvae, whatever their size, can be recognised by six microscopic teeth on the inside of the anal claw (Fig. 93). No other species of *Tinodes* has these teeth.

T. waeneri is widely distributed on stony lake shores and in large streams and rivers.

Tinodes unicolor, T. rostocki and *T. dives*

The remaining species of *Tinodes* can be grouped according to the pigmentation of the labrum. In *unicolor* the labrum is a uniform pale yellow colour (Fig. 96), in *rostocki* and *dives* it is a fairly even black or dark brown (Fig. 97), and in *pallidulus, maculicornis, assimilis* and *maclachlani* (see later notes) there is an irregular distribution of dark pigment with a concentration around the posterior-lateral points (Fig. 98). In examining the labrum for these features it is usually necessary to detach it from the head and view it against a light background, otherwise the posterior-lateral points cannot be examined properly and the dark mandibles behind the labrum may make it difficult to discern its colour pattern. These features of the labrum are apparent in 4th and 5th instar larvae.

A complicating factor with *unicolor* is that, in specimens which have been preserved for some years, the labrum may darken. Generally, however, this does not cause it to become dark enough to cause confusion with *rostocki* or *dives* (Fig. 97), nor with the species which have dark lateral points on the labrum (Fig. 98).

Apart from the labrum, the head markings in *unicolor* (Fig. 100) are not distinct from those in some of the other species (Figs 99, 105 and 106).

T. unicolor is particularly associated with calcareous streams, often where tufa is being deposited. It seems to grow slowly in winter and at this time of year its larvae and galleries are noticeably smaller than those of the faster-growing species such as *dives*.

The separation of *rostocki* and *dives* requires careful manipulation and examination of the specimen. In newly preserved specimens, the 2nd and 3rd coxopleurites are distinctly darker in *dives* (Fig. 102) than in *rostocki* (Fig. 101). This effect is produced by the thicker black horizontal bar in dives and the darker, curved plate ventral to it. There are also some features on the coxopleurite of the 1st leg which allow the separation of most specimens. The coxopleurite has a ventral notch into which the head of the coxa fits. Dorsal to this notch is a U- or V-shaped black thickening with two upwardly-projecting arms. In *rostocki* the posterior arm is always long and sharply defined (Fig. 103, arrow) whereas in *dives* the posterior arm is short or, in darkly-pigmented individuals, terminates in an area of diffuse pigment (Fig. 104, arrow). In addition, the horizontal bar connecting the base of the arms is more clearly defined in *rostocki* than in *dives*. The overall effect is for the structure to appear as a U with unequal arms in *rostocki* and as a V in *dives*. To examine these features it may be necessary to separate the coxopleurite from the pronotum. This can be done most conveniently by removing the coxopleurite still attached to the leg.

Mosely (1939) described *T. dives* as an alpine and sub-alpine species. Our finding that, in the uplands of South Wales, it occupies the moorland headwaters and gives way to *T. rostocki* in the lower wooded valleys agrees with this view. Also, the first record for *T. dives* from Ireland comes from a region with known arctic–alpine associations (O'Connor & Good 1984).

Tinodes pallidulus

T. pallidulus is separable from other species with uneven pigmentation of the labrum by the presence of a prominent large pale spot or crescentic mark on the posterior region of the frontoclypeus (Fig. 107). Occasionally, two lateral spots are present but these are always inconspicuous. By contrast, in *maculicornis, assimilis* and *maclachlani* (see below) the frontoclypeus has a line of three pale spots of more uniform size and colour (Figs 105, 106). Also, in these three species the spots on the rest of the head are more conspicuous.

In Britain, *T. pallidulus* was first recorded from two small streams in Surrey (Kimmins 1949; Hickin 1950, 1953) from which sites it has since disappeared. It has, however, recently been rediscovered in the Woodbrook, a small stream running from the Charnwood Forest in Leicestershire (Greenwood & Hobday 1988).

Tinodes maculicornis

Until recently, in the British Isles this species was known only from a few Irish records of adults dating from the turn of the century. However, it has now been rediscovered in Ireland by O'Connor & Wise (1980), who have also discussed how the larvae can be distinguished from other psychomyiids. *T. maculicornis* resembles *T. assimilis* and *T. maclachlani* in having a labrum with uneven pigmentation and a frontoclypeus with three similar pale spots in the posterior region. It differs from these two species in having no reddish pigment patch on the underside of the 2nd thoracic segment. In *assimilis* and *maclachlani* this patch (Fig. 108, arrow) can often be made more conspicuous by illuminating it from the side. We discovered that the patch fades in preservatives, such as Pampel's fluid, which contain acetic acid, and in these circumstances it cannot be used as a diagnostic feature. This is a strong argument for preserving psychomyiid larvae in alcohol.

The Irish records for *T. maculicornis* to date suggest that it is associated with the stony shores of calcareous lakes (O'Connor & Wise 1980).

Tinodes assimilis and *T. maclachlani*

As is described in the key, *T. assimilis* can be distinguished from *T. maclachlani* using the pigmentation patterns on the prolegs (Figs 109, 110) and the 1st coxopleurite (Figs 111, 112). When comparing the colour of the trochantin with the rest of the coxopleurite it is advisable to remove the head to prevent it from forming a coloured background behind the semi-transparent trochantin.

Vertical or near-vertical rock faces over which thin films of water are flowing, the so-called "hygropetric habitat" (Vaillant 1953, 1954; Hickin 1967), are typical sites for both *assimilis* and *maclachlani*. In these situations a large proportion of the rock face may be covered with larval galleries. In lowland areas *maclachlani* may extend into more typical small stream habitats. Possibily this is related to the absence of *T. dives* from lowland streams (p. 104).

Although in areas of easily-weathered rock strata psychomyiid larvae are often very abundant (Plate lB, p. 83) they are frequently overlooked, possibly as a result of the superficial resemblance of their galleries to the silt tubes of chironomids. Further notes on the biology of psychomyiids are given on pages 90, 104 and 116.

ECNOMIDAE

Although our only British species, *Ecnomus tenellus* (Rambur), has previously been included in the family Psychomyiidae, the larvae of *Ecnomus* are quite unlike psychomyiid larvae in having dorsal plates on all three thoracic segments, a lateral fringe of bristles on the abdomen (Fig. 23) and a pointed rather than a leaf-like trochantin (Fig. 79, arrow; compare with Figs 80, 81). These and other features led Lepneva (1956, 1970) to place *Ecnomus* in a separate family, an arrangement which has since been generally adopted (Wiggins 1982).

The larvae occur in lakes and slow-flowing rivers. In Wales, all three lakes where this species has been recorded are eutrophic in character (Jones 1976a; Jenkins 1977; Ormerod 1984), and we have found it on stony shores of the Shropshire Meres.

The uncertainty about the mode of life of the larvae has been resolved by Wiberg-Larsen (1993) who has shown that it constructs a silk, tube-like retreat with funnel-shaped capture surfaces at either end, strongly resembling those of small polycentropodid larvae. These structures are usually sited underneath or between stones. This, incidently, is another reason for regarding the Ecnomidae as separate from the Psychomyiidae. See pages 88, 103 and 116 for further notes on the biology of *Ecnomus tenellus*.

HYDROPSYCHIDAE

Cheumatopsyche lepida

This species differs from all other hydropsychid larvae in having a dense covering of long bristles on the dorsal anterior parts of the pronotum (Fig. 113). Long bristles are also present on the dorsal surface of the head but this feature in itself would not distinguish it from *Hydropsyche bulgaromanorum* which also has long head bristles (Fig. 128).

C. *lepida* is also notable for having extremely small posterior prosternites (Fig. 123, arrows). These structures are to be found on the underside of the 1st thoracic segment and it may be necessary to straighten the body of the larva to reveal them. All other hydropsychid species have substantially larger plates (Figs 122 and 124, arrows), which may be unpigmented, partly pigmented or wholly pigmented.

C. *lepida* is by far the smallest of the British hydropsychids and final instar larvae, when extended, measure only about 1 cm in length. This value is comfortably exceeded by all other hydropsychid species at the same stage.

C. *lepida* is usually found in small numbers in the lower reaches of large rivers (p. 97). However, it can be quite common in the outflows of lakes, such as the River Leven where it flows out of Windermere in the English Lake District (Elliott 1986). See p. 112 for further notes on the biology of C. *lepida*.

Diplectrona felix

The most obvous difference between larvae of *Diplectrona felix* and those of the remaining nine species of *Hydropsyche* is that the upper surface of the head is uniformly brown with no yellow marks (Fig. 115). In addition, the frontoclypeus is constricted at the level of the eyes (Fig. 115), the dorsal plates on the 2nd and 3rd thoracic segments are divided by transverse cleavage lines (Fig. 117, arrows), the prothoracic trochantin (a forward-projecting structure at the base of the first leg) has only a single point (Fig. 116, arrow), and the posterior prosternites are completely lacking.

In all these respects *D. felix* is quite different from the *Hydropsyche* species, where the frontoclypeus invariably carries yellow marks and has a smooth outline (e.g. Figs 130 134), cleavage lines are absent from the thoracic plates (Fig. 118), the trochantin has a double point (Fig. 114, arrow) and the posterior prosternites are always present.

D. felix is restricted to small streams and springs which remain cool in summer. It is generally regarded as having a mainly northern and western distribution in Britain (Badcock 1976). See also pages 97 and 112 for further ecological notes.

Genus HYDROPSYCHE

Hydropsyche siltalai

This is the most easily distinguished of the *Hydropsyche* species because of an absence of gills on the 7th abdominal segment (Fig. 119). In all other *Hydropsyche* larvae gills are present on this segment (Fig. 120). When trying to identify the 7th segment it is useful to bear in mind that the 8th abdominal segment which follows it has a pair of conspicuous, spiny, ventral plates (Figs 119, 120). Abdominal gills are present in *Hydropsyche* larvae from the 2nd instar onwards, so this character can be used for all but the smallest larvae (Table 1, p. 107, gives head-capsule widths for the various instars).

Fig. 121 shows a typical head pattern for *H. siltalai*. Sometimes the oral and lateral marks form a compact group of three in this way, sometimes they are fused together to form a single anterior mark. In either case confusion with other species can be avoided by reference to the gills.

H. siltalai is probably the most widespread and abundant of the British hydropsychids (Badcock 1976; Crichton et al. 1978). It lives in fast-flowing streams and rivers, often in the company of *H. pellucidula* (pp. 98–102). Where the two species occur together there is usually a marked size difference between them in the winter months. *H. pellucidula* grows rapidly in the autumn and usually passes the winter months in the 5th instar, whereas *H. siltalai* typically reaches only the 3rd instar by this time (p. 112; Figs 178, 179).

Hydropsyche bulgaromanorum and *H. contubernalis*

These two species differ from all the other species of *Hydropsyche* in having posterior prosternites which are uniformly pale (Fig. 124, arrows) rather than bicoloured (Fig. 122) or entirely dark (Fig. 141). The posterior prosternites are to be found on the underside of the first thoracic segment.

H. bulgaromanorum is easily separated from *H. contubernalis* by the possession of a conspicuous central knob on the submentum (Fig. 126), the submentum being a roughly triangular plate on the underside of the front of the head (Fig. 125). For ease of reference, on the text-figures, *Hydropsyche* species are identified by the initial letters of their specific names.

H. bulgaromanorum is unusual in having much of the dorsal head surface covered with a mat of long setae in which debris and micro-organisms become lodged, thus obscuring the underlying frontoclypeal markings (Fig. 128). If this material is cleared away the pattern revealed usually takes the form of two large pale marks linked by a narrow central connection (Fig. 129). Sometimes the oral mark is indistinct. The frontoclypeal pattern in *contubernalis* also includes anterior and posterior elements (Figs 130, 131). The lateral marks may be faintly separated from the oral one (Fig. 130).

In both species the front margin of the frontoclypeus is convex (Figs 128, 131), a feature otherwise shared only with *H. exocellata* (Fig. 144). In *contubernalis* this convexity is markedly asymmetrical (Figs 130, 131), a feature unique to this species amongst the hydropsychidae, and of value when identifying detached frontoclypeal plates in sub-fossil remains. There is also a difference in the shape of the head capsule. In *contubernalis* the head is more elongated than in *bulgaromanorum*, where the head is squarer in shape.

In Britain, *H. contubernalis* occurs in the lower reaches of large rivers, typically in the company of *Cheumatopsyche lepida*, *H. pellucidula* and sometimes also *H. siltalai* (Badcock 1976; Hildrew & Edington 1979; Edwards & Brooker 1982). Information collated by Pitsch (1993) shows a very similar ecological distribution in Central Europe.

H. bulgaromanorum is known from Britain in the form of sub-fossil larval remains (Williams 1987), and from six adult specimens, previously misidentified as *H. guttata* (Malicky 1984). The most recent of these specimens dates from 1926 and at least two of them appear to have been associated with the the the River Thames.

In continental Europe *H. bulgaromanorum* is found in the lower reaches of large rivers, often becoming the dominant species at stations immediately upstream of the estuary (Bournaud et al. 1982; Lecureuil et al. 1983; Pitsch 1993). Whether the species is now extinct in Britain or might one day be rediscovered in similar situations remains to be seen.

Hydropsyche angustipennis, H. pellucidula and *H. instabilis*

Dorsal head markings provide the most convenient means of separating the remaining six *Hydropsyche* species into two groups. In the first group, comprising *angustipennis, pellucidula* and *instabilis,* the aboral (i.e. posterior) marks on the frontoclypeus are separated from the paired lateral marks (Figs 132–134). By contrast, in the second group (*H. exocellata, fulvipes* and *saxonica*) these marks are typically joined to form a continuous sinuate pattern (Figs 144–146).

The only difficulty likely to be encountered with this initial grouping of the species is that occasionally lightly-pigmented specimens of *pellucidula* may appear to have their markings connected, and darkly pigmented specimens of *saxonica* may appear to have them separate. The identity of any such problematic specimens is, however, readily resolved by examining the ventral head markings, in which *pellucidula* shows a large, pale, triangular mark behind the submentum (Fig. 136), a feature completely lacking in *saxonica* (Fig. 149).

Hydropsyche angustipennis

H. angustipennis is readily separated from the other two species in this group (*pellucidula* and *instabilis*) by the form of its posterior prosternites (Fig. 141). These are narrow and pigmented in both their medial and lateral sections, giving an overall appearance of two narrow, strap-like structures. Some authors imply that they are completely uniform in colour. This is not quite true. In larvae which are generally rather lightly pigmented, the lateral sections of these plates may be somewhat paler than the medial sections. However, the contrast is never as great as that shown by the other two species (Figs 142, 143).

The following are additional features for distinguishing *H. angustipennis* from *H. pellucidula* and *H. instabilis.* In *angustipennis* the submentum has narrow lateral extensions (Fig. 138 compared with Figs 139 and 140); the median suture on the ventral surface of the head is very short, much less than half the width of the head (Fig. 135, arrow), and on the frontoclypeus the lateral marks are generally the most conspicuous, the aboral mark being usually rounded or triangular and diffuse in outline (Fig. 132).

The rough surface of the frontoclypeus in *angustipennis* also contrasts with the generally smooth and shiny appearance of this plate in the other two species. Pitsch (1993), using a scanning electron microscope, has shown that this difference arises partly from the fact that the frontoclypeus of *angustipennis* is uniformly covered in small bristles, whereas in the other two species these bristles are restricted to the frontoclypeal margin and to the region of the curved step-like structure which separates the front and rear sections of the plate. The frontoclypeus of *angustipennis* is also roughened by deep surface grooving.

H. angustipennis can be found in rivers and streams of all sizes. It is often encountered in the outflows of eutrophic lakes and appears to be particularly tolerant of organic pollution and high water temperatures.

Hydropsyche pellucidula and *H. instabilis*

Usually these two species can be easily separated by the shape and markings of the frontoclypeus. In *pellucidula* this plate is V-shaped with its broadest part near the anterior margin (Fig. 133). In *instabilis*, on the other hand, the plate is U-shaped, being a similar width in its posterior half as at the front (Fig. 134).

As regards the frontoclypeal markings, in *pellucidula* the aboral mark is typically in the form of a Y or an I, with the outline becoming increasingly diffuse anteriorly (Fig. 133). In *instabilis* the aboral mark is typically in the form of a distinct U or V (Fig. 134).

Other characters distinguishing *pellucidula* from *instabilis* include a submentum with lateral arms that are thinner in *pellucidula* (Fig. 139) than in *instabilis* (Fig. 140), and posterior prosternites with medial sections that are squarer in *pellucidula* (Fig. 142) than in *instabilis* (Fig. 143).

H. instabilis and *H. pellucidula* are both widespread species in Britain and are part of the common sequence of hydropsychid species in rivers (p. 97), *instabilis* occupying a zone upstream of *pellucidula*. This is evidently also the situation in Central Europe (Pitsch 1993).

Hydropsyche exocellata, H. fulvipes and *H. saxonica*

This last group of three species is distinguishable from the previous group in having a frontoclypeal pattern in which the aboral and lateral marks are joined together to form a complicated sinuate figure (Figs 144–146). In all three species, larvae can be found in which the figure is bright yellow throughout. In others some part of the pattern may be clouded; nonetheless the underlying pattern is usually detectable on close examination.

Hydropsyche exocellata

This species is clearly distinguished from the other two by the convex anterior margin of the frontoclypeus, the pustular ornamentation on the head (Fig. 144), and the finger-like marks on the ventral head surface (Fig. 147). In addition, the lateral arms of the submentum are narrower (Fig. 150) than is the case with either *fulvipes* or *saxonica* (Figs 151, 152).

The larvae of *exocellata* have been described from continental Europe by Jalón (1981) and Bournaud et al. (1982) but are not known from British material. The most recent adult records from Britain date from 1901 and came from the vicinity of the River Thames (Badcock 1976). In continental Europe, *exocellata* is found in the lower stations of large rivers (Bournaud et al. 1982; Pitsch 1993) and these would be the obvious habitats in which to search for it in Britain.

Hydropsyche fulvipes and *H. saxonica*

The most convenient feature to separate these species is to be found on the underside of the head. In *fulvipes* there is invariably a broad yellow band running behind the front margin (Fig. 148). This connects with pale bands on the sides of the head and also has a conspicuous tongue-like extension in the mid-line. Such a pattern of light markings occurs in most other *Hydropsyche* species but is conspicuously lacking in *saxonica* (Fig. 149). In *saxonica* any lightening of this region is restricted to lateral areas and sometimes a very thin pale band down the front of the median suture. Also, in ventral view the submentum of *saxonica* can be seen to have a more elongated hind projection than *fulvipes* (Fig. 152 compared with Fig. 151).

Various workers have commented on differences in the shape of the posterior prosternites in the two species. Wiberg-Larsen (1980), for example, describes the plates as "irregularly triangular" in *fulvipes* and "irregularly square" in *saxonica*. Pitsch (1993), on the other hand, attaches little importance to this shape difference and argues that the distinctive feature of *saxonica* is that the lateral sections of the prosternites are unusually dark, giving the whole structure a strap-like appearance reminiscent of *H. angustipennis*. Our material generally supports the view of Wiberg-Larsen, although the differences we found are generally less pronounced than those shown in his diagrams. If attention is focussed on the shape of the front, inside corners of the medial sclerites, these seem to be rounded in *fulvipes* (Fig. 154, arrows) but squarer in *saxonica* (Fig. 155, arrows).

Turning to the dorsal head patterns, generally we found no consistent differences between the two species. Pitsch (1993), however, makes the interesting observation that the curving "step" which separates the raised rear section of the frontoclypeus from the lower front section is less pronounced in *fulvipes* (Fig. 145) than in *saxonica* (Fig. 146), especially in the region of the mid-line. This seems to be a useful character, although some careful manipulation of the light is necessary to see the feature clearly.

Pitsch (1993) also observes that the short bulky bristles along the side of the head are dark brown in *saxonica* but paler brown in *fulvipes*. We found that this distinction also applied to our material, although again appropriate illumination is critical in making this judgement.

Finally, instar for instar, *saxonica* larvae reach a larger size than *fulvipes* larvae, a fact which becomes apparent when comparing cast larval skins.

There has been uncertainty for some years about the precise status of these two species in Britain. Some early nomenclatural confusion caused *instabilis* larvae and adults to be routinely misidentified as *H. fulvipes*, giving the impression that *fulvipes* was more widespread than was actually the case (Hildrew & Morgan 1974; Badcock 1977). Since this problem has been resolved, genuine records for *fulvipes* have been slowly accumulating. Nonetheless the species can still justifiably be described as localised.

Perceptions about the distribution of *saxonica* have also changed, but in the direction of concluding that it is more common than was previously thought. From being regarded as a very rare species in the 1970s (Badcock 1977), it has recently been shown to be widely distributed in central and western England (Blackburn & Forrest 1995). These new records have been generated mainly as the result of systematic river surveys carried out by the NERC's Institute of Freshwater Ecology. In Central Europe both species are associated with headwaters, with *saxonica* generally extending further downstream than *fulvipes* (Pitsch 1993). In Britain, it is not yet clear how the patchy distribution of these two species relates to the more widespread species–sequences in river systems.

There is much ecological information available, dealing with feeding and net-spinning, distribution and life cycles of *Hydropsyche* larvae (see pages 81, 97 and 111 in later sections of this handbook).

FEEDING BIOLOGY

There is a close relationship between the feeding techniques of the larvae and their constructional activities. For instance, the Psychomyiidae build fixed galleries on the surfaces of stones or rotting wood and scrape food from the substratum at the gallery mouth or from the walls of the tube itself. Larvae of the Philopotamidae, Hydropsychidae and Polycentropodidae all spin nets, but the form of the nets and the situations in which they are operated vary greatly from one family to another. Philopotamid nets have fine meshes and filter very small particles from a limited volume of water. Hydropsychid nets are coarser-meshed and trap proportionally larger food items from a large volume of water. Polycentropodid nets are different again and most are used as traps or snares to catch live prey from slowly-flowing or still waters. Rhyacophilid larvae make no larval construction of any kind and live by actively foraging for prey, generally in fast-flowing parts of streams.

The feeding habits of the different groups will now be examined in detail.

POLYCENTROPODIDAE

The nets spun by polycentropodid larvae consist basically of a silken tube, in which the larva rests, that may be extended at each end into two, often asymmetric, catching surfaces (Fig. 157). The nets are not usually built in fast-flowing waters and, therefore, differ in most cases from the filter-feeding devices used by the Philopotamidae and Hydropsychidae. Polycentropodid nets are generally operated as snares which capture live prey, whether it is passively drifting, actively swimming or crawling over the substratum. The mesh of the nets is generally coarser and more irregular than in the other families.

Townsend & Hildrew (1979) have shown that the nets constructed by *Plectrocnemia conspersa* vary in form according to flow rate and water depth. In flow-rates between 4.5 and 20 cm s^{-1} (the upper limit for this species) the two catching funnels are orientated into the current as if to catch drifting prey (Figs 156, 157). In slower-flowing water, net form is related to water depth. In water less than about 5 cm deep, or where a projection such as a twig comes near the surface, many of the net threads of the catching funnels are attached to the surface film (Fig. 158). In deeper water the nets are often in the form of extensive, flat areas of meshwork (up to 15 cm across) attached to stones and leaves on the stream bed (Figs 159, 160). Larvae with surface nets usually catch significantly more terrestrial prey and emerging chironomids, although after heavy rain these items are taken by nets of all types.

More is known about the net form of *Plectrocnemia conspersa* than that of the more "secretive" *Polycentropus flavomaculatus*, although the latter is one of our most abundant caddis species. The nets of *P. conspersa* are more often built in exposed and superficial situations than those of *Polycentropus*. Larvae of *Polycentropus* are, instar for instar, much smaller than *Plectrocnemia*, perhaps enabling them to use smaller crevices for net-spinning. Although Wesenberg-Lund (1911) described the nets of *P. flavomaculatus* as being shaped like "swallows' nests", they are more usually encountered as shapeless masses of silk which collapse when the supporting stone has been overturned.

While we still know rather little of the form and operation of *Polycentropus* nets in the field, the laboratory study by Dudgeon (1987) provides a quantitative account of the energetic costs of net-building. Net-spinning 5th instar larvae of *P. flavomaculatus* had metabolic rates about 17% higher than those of resting larvae, and such larvae took almost five hours to produce a "basic net". Nevertheless, the energy content of the silk (0.124 J) accounted for more than 75% of the total "cost", the increased activity using only about 0.03 J. Net-building is apparently an exhausting business for larvae and, not surprisingly, starved individuals, forced to build new nets every day, lost weight steadily and at a greater rate than other starved larvae which had been left undisturbed or that were disturbed less frequently. Conversely, larvae fed *ad libitum* built much larger nets, relative to their own body size, than less well fed individuals.

Net holders have no direct control of the rate at which prey arrive, and animals in particularly poor spots may quit their nets after some period without food (sometimes known as "giving-up-time"). Hildrew & Townsend (1980) and Dudgeon (1987) independently estimated giving-up-time in *Plectrocnemia conspersa* and *Polycentropus flavomaculatus*, respectively. Mean giving-up-time in *P. conspersa* was about 1.7 days, and Townsend & Hildrew (1980) suggested this was about appropriate to the average rate of prey capture in the field throughout the year. That is, larvae persisting in a patch for longer than 1.7 days could normally "have expected to have done better" by moving to another spot. Dudgeon (1987) suggested that prey capture rates by *Polycentropus flavomaculatus* may be much lower, and he measured mean giving-up-times in excess of 30 days. While this apparent difference between the two species could relate to differences in the conditions imposed during the experiments (e.g. flowing water for *P.*

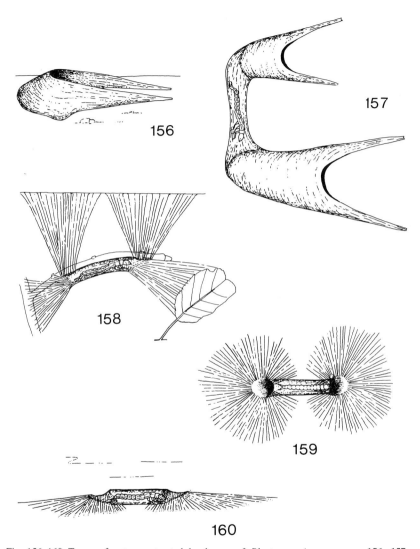

Figs 156–160. Types of nets constructed by larvae of *Plectrocnemia conspersa*. **156, 157,** catching nets constructed at water velocities between 4.5 and 20 cm s^{-1} (side and plan views). **158,** net constructed from a "perch" close to the surface or in shallower water at low water velocity (side view). **159, 160,** net constructed in deep, slowly-flowing water (plan and side views).

conspersa, still water for *P. flavomaculatus*), it could reflect real differences in the ecology of the two species. Larvae of *Plectrocnemia* are large, highly mobile, conspicuous and epibenthic, and are only abundant where fish are absent (see pp. 95–96). *Polycentropus* is much smaller, more cryptic in its habits and usually coexists with fish. Perhaps its apparently low prey capture rate and "willingness" to wait long periods without food are costs of this cryptic behaviour, while the benefit is an ability to share habitats with fish.

Holocentropus nets are to be found attached to aquatic vegetation and consist of sheet-like or funnel-shaped structures with tubular retreats (Wesenberg-Lund 1911; Alm 1926) (Fig. 161). *Cyrnus* nets are usually sited under stones, although *Cyrnus flavidus* is recorded as building conical nets on the leaves of water plants (Wesenberg-Lund 1911) (Fig. 163).

The net of *Neureclipsis bimaculata*, usually encountered in streams running out of ponds or lakes, is the largest and most distinctive of all the structures built by the Polycentropodidae and takes the form of a long, trumpet-shaped catching funnel (up to 20 cm long) with a narrower living-tube turned to point back upstream (Fig. 162) (Alm 1926; Brickenstein 1955). Petersen et al. (1984) found, upon microscopic analysis of *Neureclipsis* nets, that the walls are a loosely spun matrix of crossing strands. Large as the nets are, however, these individual strands are extremely fine (0.45 μm) and this presumably minimises the amount of silk needed in construction.

Neureclipsis larvae alter their net dimensions in response to both water velocity and seston (drifting particles) concentration (Petersen et al. 1984). The diameter of the opening of the net (and thus the area of the opening) is larger at lower velocity. Petersen et al. measured nets from the outflows of three Swedish lakes, two oligotrophic and one eutrophic. They found that net openings from the three outflows were similar at velocities above about 16 cm s^{-1}, whereas in slower currents the net openings in the two oligotrophic outflows were much larger than those in the eutrophic outflow. This points to an ability of the larvae to balance the requirements of food capture against the costs of net building and the need to reduce the hydraulic resistance of the net. Individual 5th instar larvae from the oligotrophic lake outflows weighed much less than equivalent larvae from the eutrophic outflow, yet spun much larger nets and filtered more water.

The food eaten by *Neureclipsis* is primarily of animal origin, and Petersen et al. (1984) found that the diet of 5th instar larvae in three southern Swedish lake outlets consisted entirely of zooplankton. Rossiter (1983), however, found large amounts of algal material in the guts of larvae from Welsh lake outflows. It is likely that the diet changes with season and that larvae become progressively more carnivorous as they grow, though such speculations remain to be tested.

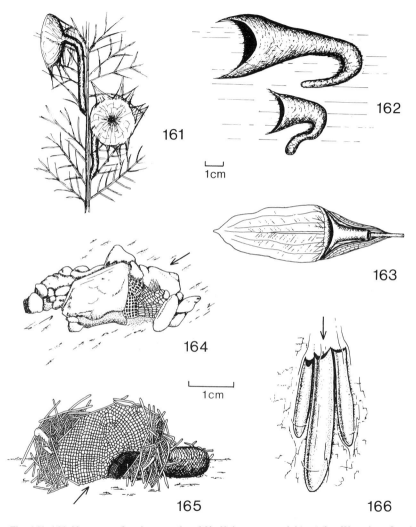

Figs 161–166. Net types of various species. **161**, *Holocentropus dubius* (after Wesenberg-Lund 1911). **162**, *Neureclipis bimaculata*. **163**, *Cyrnus flavidus* on a leaf of *Potamogeton lucens* (after Wesenberg-Lund 1911). **164**, *Hydropsyche angustipennis* net supported by stones (after Sattler 1958). **165**, *Hydropsyche angustipennis* net supported by plant fragments (after Lepneva 1970). **166**, *Philopotamus montanus*.

The other British Polycentropodidae are exclusively predatory (Percival & Whitehead 1929; Badcock 1949; Jones 1949, 1950; Tachet 1965, 1971b; Hildrew & Townsend 1976, 1982; Townsend & Hildrew 1978; Dudgeon 1987). The exact composition of the diet is variable from place to place according to the prey available. The still-water forms take a variety of rotifers, Cladocera, Copepoda and Ostracoda and, in addition, larger larvae take Oligochaeta and chironomid larvae (Higler 1978). Stream-dwelling polycentropodids take mainly larvae of Chironomidae, Ephemeroptera and Plecoptera and, in the earlier instars, benthic Crustacea. *Plectrocnemia conspersa* takes appreciable quantities of terrestrial prey and, where net threads break the surface film, any small terrestrial arthropods falling or drifting onto the surface net are attacked and spectacularly dragged down beneath the surface.

The most complete description of feeding behaviour is that of Tachet (1971a,b, 1977) for *Plectrocnemia conspersa*. He describes seven phases of predatory behaviour, beginning with the alerting of the larva to the presence of prey, through prey capture, to the final grooming and toilet. The major stimulus to prey capture is the generation of vibrations in the net threads by the struggling of prey animals after they have become entangled in the mesh. It was found that vibrations were reduced in amplitude slightly during transmission across the net, but the frequency was unchanged. Complete sequences of predatory behaviour were stimulated experimentally by vibrations in the range 0.28–7.50 Hz. The net of *P. conspersa*, therefore, seems to be used rather like that of many terrestrial spiders although, in the latter, the relevant vibration frequencies are much higher.

HYDROPSYCHIDAE

Hydropsychid nets are typically constructed in rapidly-flowing water and, in spring and summer, they are often to be seen in large numbers on the moss-covered surfaces of stones (Plate 1A, p. 83). In these situations the net consists of a simple tubular retreat, open at both ends, spun between the moss stems and extended anteriorly into an obvious arched canopy with a rear filtration area and a wide mouth. For final (5th) instar larvae the height and width of the canopy opening is up to about 1 cm. Nets are also constructed in crevices between and underneath stones where pieces of gravel or plant material are often used to support the canopy and retreat tube (Figs 164, 165). The nets are usually orientated at right angles to the water current but in very fast flows may be set obliquely (Sattler 1958). The flow of water is apparently detected by setae on the dorsal surface of the head (Kaiser 1965).

The central area of a normal hydropsychid net consists of silk strands which cross each other to produce meshes. There are two areas with rectangular or occasionally square mesh openings, divided by a mid-line with roughly diamond-shaped openings (Fig. 166). The size of the rectangular meshes does seem to vary between the species. For 5th instar larvae of species occurring in Britain, for instance, the following measurements have been made: *Hydropsyche instabilis*, 315 x 145 μm (Hildrew & Edington 1979); *H. siltalai*, 300 x 170 μm and 376 x 229 μm (Hildrew & Edington 1979 and Tachet et al. 1987, respectively); *H. pellucidula*, 368 x 240 μm and 382 x 215 μm (Hildrew & Edington 1979 and Tachet et al. 1987, respectively); *H angustipennis*, 205 x 112 μm, 259 x 170 and 170 x 85 μm (Kaiser 1965, Tachet et al. 1987 and Petersen 1987a, respectively); *H. saxonica*, 328 x 174 μm (Petersen 1987a); *Diplectrona felix*, 260 x 200 μm (Kaiser 1965). There is a good deal of variation among these measurements but *H. angustipennis* does seem to spin finer meshes than the other *Hydropsyche* species and the meshes of *Diplectrona felix* are squarer. Fey (1993) found more variation between individuals of *H. contubernalis* and of *H. pellucidula* than between the averages of the two species.

It is well established that the average mesh size of hydropsychid nets increases with instar (Sattler 1963; Kaiser 1965; Williams & Hynes 1973; Wallace 1975; Wallace et al. 1977; Malas & Wallace 1977; Wallace & Merritt 1980). For example, a typical mesh size for a 2nd instar *Hydropsyche* larva is only about 80 x 50 μm. There is also some variation of mesh size within a single net. Malas & Wallace (1977) found that the smallest meshes of two North American hydropsychid nets were in that part closest to the substratum where the water velocity would be reduced. Fey (1993) has recently confirmed this for *H. pellucidula* and *H. contubernalis*. In all nets the mesh of the outer area of the filtering canopy is quite irregular and the larva frequently allows this part to become blocked by debris.

Various environmental factors seem to influence (a) whether a net is spun at all, (b) the overall dimensions of the net, (c) the size of the individual meshes, and (d) the regularity of the meshes. Temperature and water velocity both determine the proportion of larvae that spin nets and the preferences of the various species differ (Fey & Schumacher 1978). It is often difficult to find nets at all in mid-winter, although Petersen (1987a) found a few *Hydropsyche saxonica* nets at temperatures close to 0°C in a south-Swedish stream. *Hydropsyche siltalai* began spinning nets at 2°C in the laboratory (Philipson & Moorhouse 1974), while *H. angustipennis* did not spin nets at nearly 7°C. The proportion of larvae spinning nets increases with temperature, probably reaching species–specific maxima: for instance, at about 12°C for *H. siltalai* (Philipson & Moorhouse 1974), above 23°C for *H. angustipennis* (Peterson 1987a). Fewer larvae spin nets at low than at high water velocity, though again there is variation between the species: *Hydropsyche angustipennis* has fairly low-flow preferences, a few larvae spinning nets at velocities as low as 5 cm s^{-1} (Petersen 1987a).

Overall net dimensions increase with temperature (Fey & Schumacher 1978; Petersen 1987a), and *H. saxonica* nets collected in early spring and mid-summer in southern Sweden had net mouth areas of 26–31 and 45 mm^2, respectively. Differences among the species of Hydropsychidae in the size of the rectangular, filtering meshes seem to relate to their flow preferences, species with coarser mesh favouring high velocity. There may even be some plasticity in mesh size within the species, as Boon (1984) found for a Javanese hydropsychid of the genus *Amphipsyche* that reduced the mesh aperture in its net at low water velocity.

It is also of interest that nets are sometimes found with meshes that differ from the perfection of the "normal" structure (Fig. 167). The commonest natural so-called "anomaly" concerns the shape of the meshes in the mid-line, which change from diamond-shape to irregular polygons (Fig. 168). Such anomalies occur fairly infrequently in well-fed larvae, living near their temperature optima in clean streams and rivers. Petersen (1987a) found about 10–15% of the nets of *H. saxonica* and *H. angustipennis* with mid-line anomalies under such good conditions. However, nearly half of *H. saxonica* nets had imperfections in winter at temperatures up to 4°C, while Fey & Schumacher (1978) observed increased irregularities in *Hydropsyche* nets at 30°C. Petersen (1987a) also found increased instances of anomalies in nets produced by starved larvae.

While imperfections in the net meshes occur naturally, their frequency increases greatly with various kinds of water pollution. Moreover, different kinds of anomaly occur which may even be associated with particular classes of toxin, including heavy metals and pesticides (Décamps et al. 1973; Besch

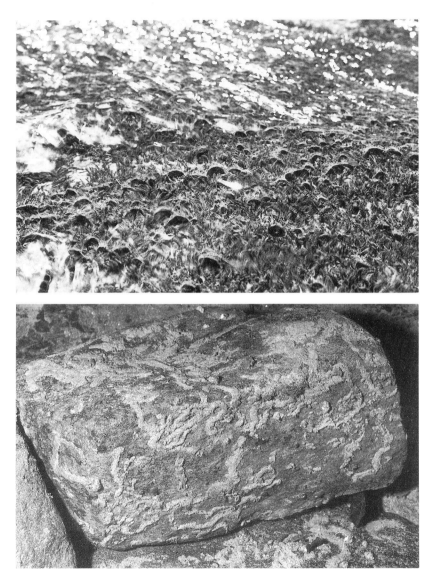

Plate 1.   **A** (*above*), nets of *Hydropsyche instabilis* constructed on moss-covered bed-rock. **B** (*below*), larval galleries of *Tinodes rostocki*.

et al. 1977; Besch et al. 1979; Petersen & Petersen 1983, 1984). "Crossover" anomalies occur in nets from streams polluted by heavy metals such as copper, lead and cadmium and became more frequent, both in terms of the proportion of nets with anomalies and in the number of anomalies per net, the closer the larvae were to sources of pollution (Petersen & Petersen 1984). A crossover anomaly occurs when one or more neighbouring rectangles are distorted by strands being fused or added over the orifice (Fig. 169). Two other net anomalies, the first where extra major strands are added over the normal net structure ("Strands crossing"; Fig. 170) and the second where major strands are fused ("Strands together"; Fig. 171), have been distinguished by Petersen (1987a). Exposure of larvae of *H. angustipennis* to pulp mill effluent, and to a chlorinated biphenolic compound that is a major constituent of that effluent, caused a great increase in the incidence of "strands crossing" and mid-line anomalies.

The feeding behaviour of *Hydropsyche siltalai* in its net has been described by Philipson (1953a). The larva holds itself in position by the anal appendages and meso- and metathoracic legs, while the prothoracic legs are held close to the undersurface of the head which is then moved rapidly from side to side, over the central area of the net. Any particles are rapidly seized using the mandibles and prothoracic legs, and inedible mineral particles are ejected from the net mouth into the current or incorporated into the net structure with silk strands. Even some apparently edible particles may be rejected in this way and it is evident that *Hydropsyche* larvae exert some selection over their diet.

The British species of Hydropsychidae are usually described as omnivorous but, in terms of the mass of food consumed, certainly take more plant or detrital material than animals (Percival & Whitehead 1929; Slack 1936; Badcock 1949; Jones 1949, 1950; Philipson 1953a; Scott 1958; Hildrew & Edington 1979; Petersen 1985, 1987b). Williams et al. (1993) found that the diet of *Diplectrona felix* included no animal material at all in a small stream in North Wales, being dominated by detritus and vascular plant remains. Petersen (1985) examined food preferences of three coexisting hydropsychids (*Hydropsyche angustipennis, H. saxonica* and *H. siltalai*) and found differences in the proportions of various types of particles in the diet of the three species, and also differences in the representation of these distinct foods in the diet compared with the seston (suspended material in the stream). In experiments, Petersen (1985) offered to larvae of one or more of the three species, sequences of (a) detrital particles only, (b) alternate detritus and *Daphnia*, or (c) *Daphnia* only. Larvae of *H. siltalai* offered detritus only consumed an average of five particles before rejecting further items. Larvae of all three species offered alternate detritus and *Daphnia* also consumed five or six detrital particles before they rejected further detritus, with no

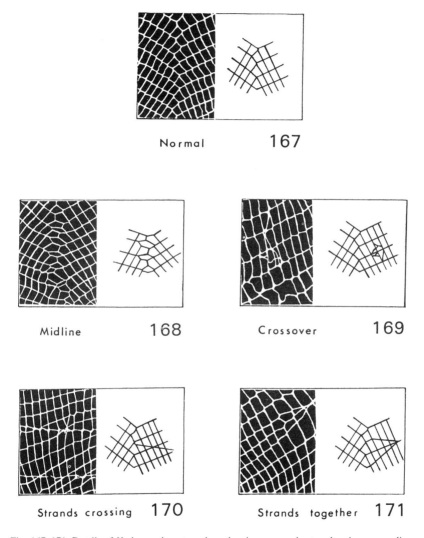

Figs 167–171. Details of *Hydropsyche* net meshes, showing a normal net and various anomalies. **167**, net with a normal mid-line. **168**, net with a mid-line anomaly. **169**, net with a crossover anomaly. **170**, net with strands crossing. **171**, net with strands together. All after Petersen (1987a).

difference among the species. These larvae continued to accept *Daphnia*, however, and an overall average (for all three species) of 62 *Daphnia* per larva was consumed after they apparently became tired of detritus! *Hydropsyche siltalai* larvae offered *Daphnia* alone managed an average of 74 items before satiation. Even more interestingly, Petersen (1985) found that, once her larvae had begun to reject detritus, they apparently continued to inspect or "taste" the particles before "making their decision". Larvae receiving only detritus continued to inspect a further 15 particles, handling each for an average of about 10 s, while those fed on alternate detritus and *Daphnia* inspected only a further two detritus particles, handling each for only about 4.5 s. The larvae do not feed indiscriminately, therefore, and drop less preferred items from their diet only when better food is abundant. Petersen (1985) found no evidence of different selective behaviour among the species, however, and interspecific discrepancies in diet are probably attributable to the occupation of slightly different microhabitats, and to distinctions in net mesh sizes.

Based on (i) observations of the "ranking" of different food types by larvae, (ii) estimates of the size (mass) of the food ration required per day, (iii) the concentration and composition of the seston available in the stream, and (iv) estimates of the volume of water filtered by a net in one day in May, Petersen (1987b) was able to predict, with remarkable accuracy, the diet of *H. siltalai* larvae. It consisted of about 90% (by weight) of detritus and diatoms, mainly because more valuable animal items were so rarely caught. At times when animal food (ranging from rotifers to insects and small crustaceans) are more abundant, however, they may briefly dominate the diet and, in terms of the carbon assimilated, material of animal origin is much more important than its simple proportion in the gut contents implies (Benke & Wallace 1980).

There is some evidence that *Hydropsyche* larvae sometimes feed independently of the net (Krawany 1930; Badcock 1949; Jones 1950; Schumacher 1970; Williams & Hynes 1973; Fuller & Mackay 1980). Petersen (1987a) found that *Hydropsyche* larvae could graze benthic algae and detritus directly from the substratum. This can occur even when larvae are holding (and feeding from) nets, but presumably is mainly important when larvae have no functional feeding net. There is some indication that this behaviour is most prevalent in the winter or early spring, and in *Hydropsyche angustipennis* more than the other species occurring in Britain.

PHILOPOTAMIDAE

Larvae of this family spin nets in the form of long (up to 2 or 3 cm), tubular bags with small mouths (Fig. 166). They are found most frequently in small upland streams where the water drains through piles of boulders. If a boulder is removed they may be seen hanging attached at the anterior end, momentarily glistening and distended with water. Nets are also occasionally found on exposed vertical rock faces.

Some older illustrations of philopotamid nets (e.g. by Ruttner 1963) show them with a large terminal hole. Although larvae frequently leave the net at this point if disturbed, no microscopical evidence for a permanent hole could be found. Indian ink suspensions introduced at the mouth of a *Philopotamus montanus* net took some minutes to disperse through the walls and did not issue through a terminal hole.

The mesh size of philopotamid nets proves to be very much smaller than was originally thought. Wallace & Malas (1976) found that the North American species *Dolophilodes distinctus* had meshes ranging from 0.2 x 2.5 µm in 2nd instar larvae up to 1.75 x 5.5 µm in 5th instar larvae. We found that nets of 5th instar larvae of *Philopotamus montanus* had a similar structure. The wall of the bag consists of a fine rectangular framework with longitudinal strands 10–13 µm apart and minor transverse strands 25–70 µm apart. There are, in addition, finer transverse strands less than 1 µm apart (Plate 2, p. 89). Each strand is made up of a double filament.

Philopotamid larvae evidently filter extremely small particles. The most extensive data on their diet are those of Wallace et al. (1977) and Malas & Wallace (1977). They show that the average size of detritus particles in the guts of *Dolophilodes distinctus* was 5 µm² with some less than 1 µm². Information on the British species is rather limited although there is every indication that detritus and diatoms are the main dietary constituents. Philipson (1953b) and Jones (1949) found these items in the guts of *Wormaldia subnigra* and *Philopotamus montanus*, respectively. Our own observations show that *P. montanus* guts were filled with a mass of gritty detritus and diatoms, with a very few small fragments of higher plant tissue. Recently Williams et al. (1993) also found that diatoms and detritus dominated the gut contents of both *Philopotamus montanus* and *Wormaldia occipitalis* in the same Welsh stream.

The uniformly small size of particles in the guts of philopotamid larvae is consistent with the fine mesh of their nets. It seems that the absence of any larger particles in the diet is due, firstly, to the overall shape of the net and, secondly, to the behaviour of the larva. The net mouth is very restricted and, because of the flow patterns created, we found it quite difficult to introduce larger particles into the net using a pipette. When we did succeed in introducing fragments of moss or small live animals such as chironomid larvae, the caddis always vigorously ejected them from the net mouth. Normally, fine food particles which collect on the inner wall are gathered by downward sweeping movements of the brush-like labrum (Philipson 1953b).

ECNOMIDAE

It is now clear that larvae of the only British species, *Ecnomus tenellus* (and probably most or all other Ecnomidae), are net-spinning predators (Stroot et al. 1988; Wiberg-Larsen 1993). Wiberg-Larsen (1993) kept 3rd to 5th instar larvae from Danish lakes in the laboratory and all spun nets. These are commonly built underneath or between stones, but may also be found among submersed vegetation, and are easily destroyed and thus overlooked when turning stones over in the field. The nets are similar to those of several polycentropodids, consisting of a simple silken tube, in which the larva rests, with a funnel-shaped structure at either end, in which the prey are captured. The retreat tubes of fully grown larvae were up to 25 mm in length while the funnel structures could be up to 60 mm in diameter. Larvae quickly attack prey trapped in the threads. A wide variety of small invertebrates have been found in gut contents, including Nematoda, Oligochaeta, Tardigrada, small crustaceans (Copepoda, Cladocera and Ostracoda), insect larvae (Ephemeroptera and Chironomidae) and Hydrachnellae (Wiberg-Larsen 1993). Larger prey items, offered in laboratory experiments, were only part-ingested so that easily recognised sclerotized parts would be missing from gut contents.

Plate 2.   Part of the net of *Philopotamus montanus* at low magnification (*above*; the scale line = 40 µm) and at high magnification (*below*; the scale line = 4 µm). (SEM photograps by D. Windsor).

PSYCHOMYIIDAE

These gallery-building caddis larvae are particularly characteristic of streams running over easily weathered rocks, and lakes with stony substrata. Psychomyiid galleries are fixed, tunnel-like, structures (Plate 1B, p. 83) and thus contrast with both the nets and transportable cases of other caddis larvae. They have been described by Berg (1938), Danecker (1961), Hickin (1967), Alderson (1969) and Hasselrot (1993). In cross-section the gallery walls form an arch with a sufficiently large internal diameter to allow the larva within to turn round on itself. The gallery length varies, according to species, from two to seven times the larval length.

The galleries are constructed from fragments of mineral or other materials held together by silk. In *Tinodes waeneri,* which uses mineral particles, Jones (1976a) has shown that there is some selection of particle size. 4th instar larvae were found to choose particles of 0.2 and 0.5 mm diameter whilst 5th instars chose those of 1 mm. This selection is probably related to the mandibular gape of the larvae. Alderson (1969) found that sand grains were the most frequently used material in the field, especially for those species inhabiting streams and rivers. In thin water films running over rocks, however, he found that the galleries of *Tinodes dives, T. maclachlani, T. assimilis* and *T. unicolor* consisted largely of faecal pellets. If there is a thick algal mat on the substratum, pieces may be bitten off and incorporated into the gallery. The two species of *Lype* are distinctive in that they build their galleries on submerged branches and use fragments of woody material. These may be derived from faecal pellets or directly from the substratum. The galleries are usually broader at the anterior end than at the posterior end.

Descriptions of the feeding of psychomyiid larvae have been given by Danecker (1961), Jones (1976b) and, most extensively for the stream-dwelling species, by Alderson (1969). The larva partially emerges from the front of the gallery and grazes material from the substratum. In this position it can quickly withdraw if disturbed since the anal hooks maintain a firm grip on the floor of the gallery. The larva scrapes at the substratum with its mandibles, which in consequence are often found to be worn down at the tip. The labrum is held over the mandibles while the maxillae extend below, thus forming a cavity in which food is collected. The fine hairs on the maxillae and on the lower surface of the mandibles probably serve to prevent the loss of small particles. The tip of the right mandible scrapes food along a groove in the left mandible and it is conveyed from here to the mouth. When the food supply is exhausted around the gallery mouth, the larva demolishes the hind end of the gallery and extends it at the front. The galleries thus gradually change position as feeding progresses.

The larvae in this family fall into two groups based on their diet. *Lype* species feed on wood and the others mainly on algae, although animal remains have been recorded from the gut of *Tinodes waeneri* (Dunn 1954). Since the larvae feed by scraping surfaces, they inevitably ingest a good deal of inorganic matter. Becker (1990) found that *Tinodes rostocki* took mainly diatoms in a small German stream, and that these reached seasonal maxima in the gut contents in spring and autumn, coinciding with blooms in the stream. *Tinodes rostocki* took very few cyanobacteria, however, despite their abundance on the stone surfaces.

Recent work by Hasselrot (1993), on *Tinodes waeneri* larvae in the littoral of Lake Erken in Sweden, raises some interesting new questions on the feeding and role of this psychomyiid in lakes. Using novel methods of observing larvae inside their galleries he finds that larvae feed actively off the inside of the gallery walls and by biting holes in the silk (which are then rapidly repaired by the addition of new silk). In fact, he found that *T. waeneri* larvae rarely emerge from their galleries at all, thus casting doubt on the importance of epilithic algae on the substratum around the galleries as food for this species. Nutrient concentrations (phosphorous and ammonium) were high inside the galleries and the chlorophyll content of the gallery walls was high. Hasselrot (1993) suggests that dense populations of *T. waeneri* can exist in oligotrophic lakes because the algae/gallery/larva system is analogous to the tight, nutrient recycling, symbiotic systems of coral reefs that are found in ultraoligotrophic sea water. Others have found that *Tinodes* larvae rarely seem to come out of their galleries (for *Tinodes rostocki* see Becker 1993), although Hasselrot's is the most "radical" explanation put forward so far. Although algae "cultured" on the gallery may play some role in the nutrition of populations in oligotrophic situations, this does not seem to provide a complete explanation for the distribution and abundance of all psychomyiids, however, nor even of all *Tinodes waeneri* populations. For instance, *Tinodes waeneri* is absent or scarce in the most oligotrophic lakes and is numerous, in contrast, in eutrophic systems. Similarly, stream-dwelling psychomyiids are only found in relatively productive waters. More directly, Dall et al. (1984) estimated that the production of *T. waeneri* in the Danish Lake Esrom could be supported by epilithic algal production alone. Hasselrot (1993) also suggests that the meandering shape of *T. waeneri* galleries on rock surfaces is mainly caused by interactions between neighbouring larvae (i.e., because "contestants" turn away from each other) rather than by the larva moving its gallery in search of food. Clearly, the biology of psychomyiid larvae continues to provide many fascinating questions.

Alderson (1969) has provided evidence from his studies in South Wales that some psychomyiid species are associated with particular algal communities. For example, *Tinodes unicolor* typically occurs in highly calcareous streams (calcium concentration > 60 mg l⁻¹) and feeds on the blue-green alga *Phormidium incrustratum*. This alga is found embedded in calcite incrustations and is involved in their deposition (Fritsch 1950). The larvae appear to gain access to the algal filaments by using an acid secretion which dissolves the surrounding calcite.

By contrast *Psychomyia pusilla* is particularly associated with sites where the spring diatom community is well-developed. This community includes species such as *Cymbella, Gomphonema, Navicula* and *Achnanthes*. The acceleration of growth rate of *Psychomyia* in April and May takes place when the larvae are feeding on the spring bloom of diatoms.

RHYACOPHILIDAE

Rhyacophila larvae neither spin nets nor build fixed galleries but are free-living. They appear to be actively foraging predators (Siltala 1907; Percival & Whitehead 1929; Slack 1936; Nielsen 1942; Badcock 1949; Jones 1949; Scott 1958). Major sources of prey are chironomid larvae and larvae of *Baetis* and *Simulium*. Diet varies, however, with the availability of prey. We have found that small *Hydropsyche* larvae are quite frequently taken and Fox (1978) showed that *Rhyacophila* would eat eggs of the bullhead (*Cottus gobio*). Otto (1993) reported that *Rhyacophila nubila*, which occurs in Sweden, was a freely roving predator when feeding on blackflies, but that it "ambushed", from a shelter, fast-moving prey such as mayflies. He found that hungry larvae were more active than well-fed individuals and that larvae, in a similar nutritional condition, from a fishless stream were more active than those from a stream with fish. Most remarkably he found that *R. nubila* larvae would often return to a "home stone" and that this stone was often attached, by silk, to the stream bed. Malmqvist (1993) also studied *R. nubila* in Sweden, plus a second species *R. fasciata*. Periods of active wandering by both species were primarily nocturnal and larvae subsequently returned to the same resting site. Such sites were usually successfully defended by "residents" against other intruding larvae.

A fairly large proportion of individuals, especially the smaller instars, may be found with plant material in the gut. This could represent the remains of the gut contents of herbivorous prey animals (Nielsen 1942) but it seems more likely that the larvae sometimes actively feed on the algae and moss on stones. The gut contents of *Rhyacophila* larvae may present particular problems of interpretation because they frequently engulf only parts of their prey. This is probably due to their relatively small head-width and gape (Martin & Mackay 1982).

HABITAT DISTRIBUTION

The distribution of the species can be considered at a number of different spatial scales. Firstly, they sometimes show distinctive geographic patterns within the British Isles and, where possible, we have mentioned such cases in the taxonomic section. However, we feel that distribution maps, for all but the commonest species, would be more misleading than helpful. Secondly, patterns of distribution along river systems are of interest and there is now a good deal of information on this aspect. Thirdly, the micro-distribution patterns of larvae on the stream or river bed have received much attention. Consequently it is these last two aspects of species distribution which are dealt with in particular here.

In British rivers there are well-marked downstream sequences of species in the families Hydropsychidae, Polycentropodidae (Figs 172, 173) and Psychomyiidae. These distribution patterns seem to be proximally linked mainly with physical factors. Within each family there would seem to be an adaptive radiation of species in relation to the various factor gradients down the length of watercourses.

At the microhabitat level, the distribution patterns of species can be related to variations in such factors as water velocity, substratum, food supply and competitors.

POLYCENTROPODIDAE

Some polycentropodid larvae, including *Cyrnus flavidus*, *C. insolutus*, *Holocentropus stagnalis* and *H. dubius*, appear to be restricted in Britain to still water. *Neureclipsis bimaculata* is usually found in streams draining from lakes while the remaining species are found in both standing and running water.

In rivers, there is a clear sequential pattern of species, with *Plectrocnemia conspersa* or *P. geniculata* being normally found in small headwater streams and replaced downstream by *Polycentropus flavomaculatus* (Edington 1968; Edington & Hildrew 1973). A third species of *Plectrocnemia, P. brevis*, has been rediscovered in Britain by Wallace & Wallace (1983) and taken in sites in South Devon, North Wales, Cheshire and Merseyside. It is found in tiny trickles, shaded by trees and usually with hard water depositing calcium carbonate (tufa). *Plectrocnemia conspersa* is often very abundant in acidic or metal-polluted streams (Hildrew & Townsend 1976, 1982; Townsend et al.

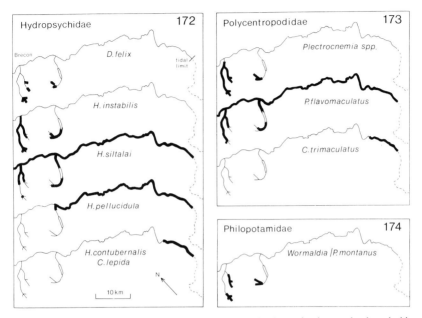

Figs 172–174. Distribution of net-spinning caddis larvae in the main river and selected side tributaries in the River Usk, South Wales.

1983; Darlington et al. 1987; Gower & Darlington 1990; Gower et al. 1994). The first point of interest is that the species seems extremely tolerant of metal pollution (certainly including copper, zinc, aluminium and iron) and acidity. Its abundance at such sites, however, may be attributable to the absence of fish (Hildrew et al. 1983; Schofield et al. 1988), that are themselves susceptible to acidic or metal-polluted water but are normally effective predators of the large larvae of *Plectrocnemia*. Fish predation does not seem absolutely to exclude *Plectrocnemia*, however, although the maximum density of populations coexisting with fish is greatly reduced. Further, Otto (1985) suggested that the distribution of polycentropodids was related to the size of prey available in different streams, *Plectrocnemia* being found in small streams where mean prey size is supposedly large.

Cyrnus trimaculatus usually appears in the lower reaches of larger rivers. Fig. 173 shows a typical polycentropodid distribution pattern from the River Usk in South Wales. This pattern has been associated with physiological differences between the species, since Philipson & Moorhouse (1976) have shown that *Polycentropus flavomaculatus* is more tolerant than *Plectrocnemia conspersa* of the high temperatures and decreased oxygen concentrations, that characterise the lower reaches of rivers.

Polycentropodids, in common with larvae of Hydropsychidae, are sometimes markedly abundant in streams flowing from ponds and lakes. This is true of *Polycentropus flavomaculatus* but, in particular, *Neureclipsis bimaculata* is a lake-outlet specialist and rarely occurs anywhere else. Dense aggregations of *Neureclipsis* occur immediately downstream of many lakes and larval populations usually decline within a few hundred metres. A proximal reason for this lies in the behaviour of adult females, who fly upstream until the lake is reached and then lay their eggs mainly on submerged wood (Statzner 1978). Food supply, in the form of suspended material (seston) from the lake, must ultimately play a role, however, and Richardson (1984) found that lake-outlet seston supported a growth rate of *N. bimaculata* ten times higher than that achieved on equivalent material from further downstream.

The microdistribution of polycentropodid larvae is related primarily to water velocity. Edington (1965, 1968) found that *Plectrocnemia conspersa* and *Polycentropus flavomaculatus* were most common in stream pools, in marked contrast with hydropsychid and philopotamid species, which were characteristic of rapids. This commitment to slow flow-rates is reflected in the mechanical properties of the net. For example, nets of *Plectrocnemia conspersa* disintegrate when subjected to velocities in excess of 20 cm s^{-1}. There are also major differences in respiratory physiology between polycentropodid and hydropsychid larvae. Philipson (1954) found, for instance, that *Polycentropus flavomaculatus* could utilise oxygen at relatively low concentrations, even in still water.

Even within the tolerable range of water velocity, up to about 20 cm s^{-1}, the distribution of *Plectrocnemia conspersa* larvae is not uniform. They tend to aggregate in parts of the stream bed where benthic prey density is highest (Hildrew & Townsend 1976, 1982), and in these areas larvae may fight over net-spinning sites. In a laboratory stream, net-holders were observed to defend their territories from intruding larvae, with both individuals rearing up "face-to-face" and striking at each other with mandibles open. The larger of the two larvae normally won possession of the net, usually without obvious injury to either contestant (Hildrew & Townsend 1980). Otto (1989) found that residents had some advantage over intruders when both larvae were of a similar size. Field experiments in a fishless stream confirmed that net-spinning sites may limit local densities of larvae in such favoured circumstances (Lancaster et al. 1988).

HYDROPSYCHIDAE

In the Hydropsychidae the typical order of first appearance from source to mouth in sizeable unpolluted rivers in Britain is: *Diplectrona felix, Hydropsyche instabilis, Hydropsyche siltalai, Hydropsyche pellucidula, Hydropsyche contubernalis* and/or *Cheumatopsyche lepida* (Mackereth 1960; Edington 1968; Edington & Hildrew 1973; Badcock 1975, 1976; Boon 1979; Hildrew & Edington 1979; Brooker & Morris 1980; Edwards & Brooker 1982). Fig. 172 illustrates this sequence in the River Usk. Some more recent studies on continental Europe basically confirm this conclusion but also place it in a wider taxonomic and geographic context (Tachet et al. 1992; Pitsch 1993). Two species previously recorded (but now probably extinct here), *Hydropsyche exocellata* and *H. bulgaromanorum*, are confirmed as large river species, along with others from western Europe never taken in Britain. Some records also suggest that *Cheumatopsyche lepida* may also penetrate further upstream than is the case in the Usk (Edwards & Brooker 1982; Pitsch 1993). Elliott (1986) found that *C. lepida* was abundant in the River Leven, the lake-outflow of Windermere in the English Lake District. *Hydropsyche saxonica* is now known to be patchy but widespread in Britain. Pitsch (1993) found it to be a species of small, lowland streams in Germany, and Petersen (1987a) found it in similar places in southern Sweden but describes it as a particularly rheophilic (preferring fast currents) species. In Britain, Blackburn & Forrest (1995) report that *H. saxonica* commonly co-occurs with *H. siltalai* and *H. instabilis*, but usually contributes a small proportion of the total hydropsychid assemblage. *Hydropsyche fulvipes* is a rare, local species in Britain where it is found in very small (first order) streams, similar to its distribution in Germany (Pitsch 1993).

The other common British hydropsychid, *H. angustipennis*, is sometimes found in the lower reaches of large rivers but typically occurs in eutrophic streams, particularly the outflows of ponds and lakes. This distribution may be related to its known tolerance of high temperatures, low oxygen concentrations and low water velocities (Ambühl 1959; Philipson & Moorhouse 1974; Jakob et al. 1984).

Physicochemical environmental factors change along the length of streams and rivers and, perhaps not surprisingly, species occupying a particular position in the longitudinal sequence seem to have appropriate suites of physiological and behavioural characteristics. For instance, we have found that *D. felix, H. instabilis* and *H. pellucidula* exhibit differences in their respiratory-rate/temperature relationships which suggest that they are adapted to progressively higher summer temperatures. In the River Usk system, *D. felix* is characteristic of small streams with summer maxima up to 15 °C and small daily ranges. Further downstream, *H. instabilis* stations have

higher summer maxima and larger daily ranges. In the main river, the
H. pellucidula stations also have high maxima but much-reduced daily
ranges. As might be expected, there are some departures from this general
pattern. For example, in headstreams which run from open moorland into
wooded gorges, and where summer temperatures decrease rather than
increase downstream, *Hydropsyche instabilis* occurs upstream of *Diplectrona
felix*.

Roux et al. (1992) have recently extended our knowledge of the metabolic
rate of hydropsychid larvae in relation to temperature and, among the species
they assessed, were *H. contubernalis, H. pellucidula* and *H. siltalai*. They
found that the amplitude of metabolic rates over a range of temperatures was
wider in species living in large rivers than in those characteristic of
headwaters. Further, Tachet et al. (1992) suggest that hydropsychid species
are ordered in a downstream sequence according to their ability to spin a
normal net at low current velocities. Downstream species, including the
British *H. contubernalis*, spin most nets at about 15 cm s^{-1}, compared with
optimum velocities of up to about 40 cm s^{-1} for the headwater species
H. siltalai. Further, Becker (1987) reported that *Hydropsyche contubernalis*
has recolonised the middle Rhine before *H. pellucidula* because the former is
more tolerant of reduced oxygen concentration in the water, being able to
build nets, grow and develop normally at only 50% of air-saturation.
Evidence is thus accruing impressively that the downstream sequence of
species is associated with physiological traits enabling the species of large
rivers to tolerate relatively high temperature, low water velocity and low
oxygen characteristics. The key question remaining, however, is whether the
observed distribution patterns are determined by species reacting
"independently" to the environmental gradient, or whether interspecific
competition plays any role.

We earlier noted the occurrence of imperfections in the nets of
hydropsychid larvae in relation to water quality. Clearly this raises the
possibility that the Hydropsychidae could be of use in the detection and
assessment of pollution. In terms of simple organic enrichment and oxygen
depletion we have already seen that the two most tolerant species are
H. angustipennis and *H. contubernalis*. The conspicuous abundance of
H. angustipennis in small streams and rivers, in relation to other species such
as *H. instabilis, H. siltalai* or *H. pellucidula*, is a fairly good indicator of
modest organic enrichment (though not of gross pollution). Other forms of
pollution may be indicated by morphological changes to larvae as well as by
anomalies in their nets. Two particular abnormalities have been found. The
anal papillae of normal animals are fairly small, pale and transparent (Fig.
22). With increasing physiological stress they become, firstly, extruded and
prominent with slight pigmentation and then, progressively, darker and

reduced until they appear shrivelled and almost black. The ventral abdominal gills, which are tufted and white or pale in colour in healthy larvae, can also become darkened and reduced almost to simple stumps. A variety of pollutants/effluents have been shown to cause these changes including chlorine (in *H. pellucidula*; Camargo 1991), cadmium (in *H. siltalai* and *H. contubernalis*; Vuori 1994), copper (in *H. saxonica* and *H. angustipennis*; Petersen 1986), pulp waste (in *H. contubernalis* and *H. pellucidula*; Vuori 1992) and acidity with increased metals (*H. siltalai* and *H. angustipennis*; Vuori 1995). These changes are first apparent at sub-lethal concentrations of pollutants but death soon occurs in severe cases. Again, *H. angustipennis* has been found markedly more tolerant, at least of copper (Petersen 1986) and acidity/metals (Vuori 1995), than other species.

The flow preferences of hydropsychids also influence their microdistribution (for instance, their relative abundance in riffles and pools) as well as the sequence of species along rivers. Traditionally regarded as fast-flow specialists, they are complementary, both in distribution and physiological attributes, to the pool-living polycentropodids (Philipson 1954, 1969; Edington 1965, 1968). As discussed above, however, it is now clear that even within the Hydropsychidae a range of water-velocity preferences occur. For instance, the preference for slower flow of *Hydropsyche pellucidula* may facilitate its coexistence with the strictly rheophilic *H. siltalai*, within the same river reach, by their differential use of a mosaic of habitat patches with different hydraulic properties (Philipson & Moorhouse 1974; Boon 1978; Hildrew & Edington 1979). In this context, Boon (1987) suggests that the increase of *H. siltalai* and the decline of *H. pellucidula* downstream from the new Kielder Water reservoir may be explained by changes in the flow habitat. Joensuu & Vuori (1993) also found that the large river species *H. contubernalis* prefers lower water velocities to *H. siltalai*.

As in the Polycentropodidae, there is evidence that antagonistic behaviour is important in determining microdistribution and may limit local densities of larvae. Johnstone (1964) first demonstrated that hydropsychid larvae could stridulate. The sound is produced by the larva rubbing a scraper on the front femur (Plate 3, p. 100) across a file on the underside of the head (Plate 4, p. 101). The scraper takes the form of a protuberance bearing ridges of cuticle and the file is an area of cuticle with a number of wave-like folds on it. Jansson & Vuoristo (1979) provided experimental evidence that stridulation is used by larvae occupying nets, as a means of repelling intruders, and they found that defenders which failed to stridulate were more likely to be evicted.

There remains some doubt as to the most significant frequency in the sounds emitted by hydropsychid larvae. Jansson & Vuoristo's analysis suggested that most of the energy lay below a frequency of 4 kHz. However, Silver (1980), using high-frequency equipment, reported strong ultrasonic

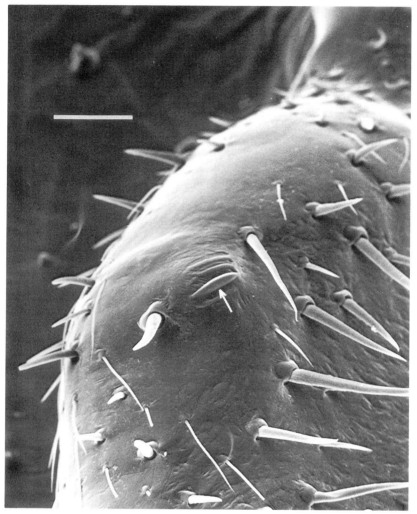

Plate 3.   Stridulatory apparatus in *Hydropsyche siltalai*; the arrow (centre picture) points to
the scraper on the prothoracic femur; the scale line = 100 μm.
(SEM photograph by S. C. Silver).

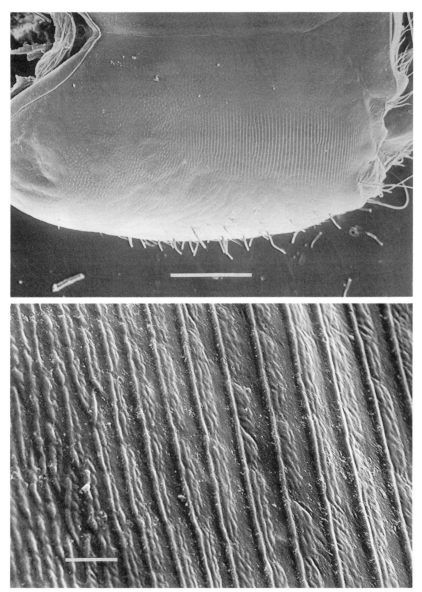

Plate 4.   Stridulatory apparatus in *Hydropsyche siltalai*. *Above*: general view of the file on the ventral surface of the head; the scale line = 250 μm. *Below*: enlarged view of the file; the scale line = 20 μm. (SEM photographs by S. C. Silver).

components up to 90 khz. She makes the interesting suggestion that such high frequencies might make possible the clear detection of oscillatory movements in the water at a range up to 2 cm, leaving the animals deaf to the background noise in a fast-flowing and turbulent stream. As yet, however, there is no clear evidence of whether the high or low frequency components of the sound predominate, or of how they are detected by other individuals.

Fighting over nets is now well-known in hydropsychids and involves biting and pushing by both residents and intruders, as well as stridulation. Englund & Olsson (1990) found that the outcome of such fights was largely determined by relative body size, with residents at an advantage over intruders when the contestants are otherwise fairly evenly matched. Contrary to some theoretical expectations, however, neither the amount of silk in the net nor the previous food intake rate affected the tenacity of the resident's defence. In the contests observed by Englund & Olsson (1990), stridulation occurred sometimes in the early stages of a contest, then always by the resident, but most frequently by the winner after the fight was over.

Such net defence is a form of territoriality and serves to space larvae out on the substratum (Plate 1A, p. 83). The spacing of hydropsychid larvae also seems to be sensitive to food supply, larvae being more aggressive when they are hungry, leading to bigger nearest-neighbour distances (Matczak & Mackay 1990). The importance of interference-competition for space in determining food supply has further been demonstrated by Englund (1991) for *Hydropsyche siltalai*. In simple but elegant experiments he demonstrated that larvae holding nets downstream from dense aggregations of conspecifics grew more slowly than those upstream of similar aggregations. Food concentration in the drift (in the form of small animal prey) was reduced behind aggregations, by about 50%, and current velocity was also reduced. Nets of competitors upstream thus acted as "hydraulic engineers" to the detriment of animals downstream. It is noteworthy that nets are often very crowded together side by side whereas longitudinal distances are generally greater, sometimes producing nets in rows across suitable substrata. Where food supply is particularly rich, as in lake outflows for instance, nearest-neighbour densities seem to decline and densities can be very great indeed.

PHILOPOTAMIDAE

Philopotamus montanus and *Wormaldia* spp. occur typically in the rapids of headwaters and tributaries, particularly where water runs vertically down through piles of boulders (Fig. 174) (Edington 1965, 1968). Philipson (1953b) has shown in the laboratory that larvae of *W. subnigra* require high water velocities for net-spinning.

The rather sparse distribution records available for *Chimarra marginata* suggest that, compared with the other philopotamids, it extends into larger rivers.

ECNOMIDAE

The larvae of *Ecnomus tenellus* have been collected from the River Thames and from eutrophic lakes in Wales and Shropshire. On the continent of Europe it is common in large rivers such as the Rhine and Meuse (Stroot et al. 1988). Nets may be spun among macrophytes but are common on or beneath stones and even among growths of freshwater sponges (Jenkins 1977). This is a locally abundant and extremely widespread caddis, occurring from western Europe to Japan, and from Scandinavia south to Sri Lanka. It is remarkable that so little is still known of its biology.

PSYCHOMYIIDAE

The most widespread and abundant species of psychomyiid in Britain is *Tinodes waeneri*, which is largely a resident of the stony and wave-washed shores of meso- to eutrophic lakes.
Our information about the habitat distribution of the stream-dwelling Psychomyiidae derives mainly from the unpublished work of Alderson (1969) and the records collected by Jenkins (1977). These studies relate principally to South Wales and further work is needed to discover whether the patterns described are of general occurrence.
Psychomyiids are usually scarce or absent in streams with soft or acidic water. In the more productive and base-rich streams and rivers of the uplands of South Wales the psychomyiids show a succession of species resembling that seen in the net-spinners. *Tinodes maclachlani* and *T. assimilis* are typically found in situations where small streams or seepages flow in thin films over vertical rock faces. These rock faces often form the side walls of larger streams or rivers and correspond to the "hygropetric habitat" of continental workers (Vaillant 1953, 1954). In the main channels of upland streams, *T. dives* occupies the moorland headwaters but is replaced by *T. rostocki* where the stream flows through woodland (Alderson 1969).
In running waters, *T. waeneri* may appear downstream of these other two species. Although *Psychomyia pusilla* may coexist with *T. dives* in the headwaters, it also extends into larger streams and rivers (Alderson 1969; Jenkins 1977). *T. unicolor* must be considered as something of a special case because of its association with highly calcareous waters. All of the nineteen sites in South Wales where Alderson collected this species had a calcium concentration in excess of 60 mg l⁻¹. Alderson (1969) argued that these patterns were related most directly to the distribution of algal communities, and probably only indirectly to physical variables. Apparently interspecific competition may also play a part in determining distribution. In lowland streams in South Wales, where *T. dives* is absent, *T. machlachlani* extends its range from rock-face sites into the main channels of streams.
Intraspecific competition for space among these gallery-building larvae has been described for British and North American psychomyiids (Alderson 1969; Hart 1983; Hasselrot 1993). This could produce the commonly-occurring spacing between galleries. Becker (1993) cleaned stone surfaces in a small German stream and expected them to be recolonised by small larvae of *Tinodes rostocki* displaced by larger larvae from undisturbed stones nearby. Recolonisation, however, was by larvae that were *larger* than the population average. Clearly, contest competition among psychomyiids requires further work.

RHYACOPHILIDAE

Rhyacophila larvae are probably the caddis most restricted to conditions of high current-speed. Their commitment to fast flow-rates reflects both the distribution of their food supply and their physiological limitations. Philipson (1954) showed that, in still water, *R. dorsalis* was immobilised even at high oxygen concentrations, and Ambühl (1959), working on *R. nubila*, found that the normal rate of oxygen consumption was not maintained when either water velocity or oxygen concentration was reduced. It is significant that the larvae do not undulate the abdomen, as do those of Hydropsychidae and Polycentropodidae. Such movements have a ventilatory function in the latter two families and their undulatory rate is increased under respiratory stress (Fox & Sidney 1953; Philipson 1954, 1978; Ambühl 1959; Philipson & Moorhouse 1974, 1976).

Scott (1958) found that *Rhyacophila* was most common in current-speeds of 80–90 cm s⁻¹. He also found that *Rhyacophila dorsalis* was a frequent inhabitant of the mossy upper surfaces of stones. On stones without moss the larvae were found only on the lower surfaces. Dorier & Valliant (1954) found *Rhyacophila* larvae in water velocities up to 125 cm s⁻¹ in the field, and in the laboratory showed that larvae were not dislodged until the current speed reached 200 cm s⁻¹.

No detailed comparisons have been made of the habitats occupied by the four *Rhyacophila* species found in Britain.

LIFE HISTORIES

All of the families considered here have basically similar life-history patterns. The adult female lays eggs in a plate-like mass, usually on a submerged boulder. After hatching, the larvae develop to maturity through a series of five instars. As with all insects, the change from one instar to the next involves a marked increase in size, and the progression of the population through successive instars can be monitored by making measurements of head-widths. The available information on head-widths for various species is set out in Table 1. The life-cycle reconstructions given in Figs 175 to 188 have been made on this basis.

Fully developed (5th instar) larvae construct a stony pupal case. These pupal cases can be confused with the larval cases of case-bearing caddis. However, they differ from them in being firmly attached to stones and in having no obvious head-opening. In some species, e.g. *Polycentropus flavomaculatus* and *Rhyacophila dorsalis*, 5th instar larvae may occupy pupal cases during the winter and the pupal change is delayed until the following spring. Such larvae are usually referred to as resting larvae.

During the pupal period, which lasts about three weeks, the major structural changes necessary to produce the adult take place. Towards the end of this period, the adult genitalia are sufficiently well formed within the pupal skin to allow them to be used for identification purposes. This is useful because it also allows the identification of the last larval skin which remains in the pupal case.

Adult caddis are most frequently encountered in summer. A few species, however, have long flight-periods and occur in every month of the year except December and January. The pattern of emergence varies from one species to another and also, on a geographical basis, for any one species. Emergence patterns can be studied using emergence traps fixed over suitable habitats. Light-trap captures will also provide information about flight patterns but will not attract day-flying species such as *Diplectrona felix*.

A one-year life cycle is typical of the majority of species. The main variations occur when some individuals in a population require a second year to complete development, or where in favourable conditions a second generation can be completed within a single year.

Related species living in the same habitat often have staggered larval growth-periods. This may not be simply fortuitous and probably serves to reduce inter-specific competition. Such species-pairs include *Hydropsyche siltalai* and *H. pellucidula*, *Holocentropus picicornis* and *H. dubius*, *Psychomyia pusilla* and *Tinodes dives*.

Table 1. Available data on head-capsule widths (range, mm) of caseless caddis larvae of different instars.

Species	1	2	Instars 3	4	5
Rhyacophila dorsalis	0.27-0.30	0.39-0.45	0.57-0.64	0.81-0.90	1.18-1.45
Rhyacophila munda	0.26-0.28	0.37-0.41	0.51-0.58	0.78-0.90	1.15-1.33
Polycentropus flavomaculatus	0.18-0.27	0.30-0.40	0.41-0.65	0.68-1.05	1.10-1.60
Polycentropus kingi	–	–	–	–	1.50-1.66
Plectrocnemia conspersa	0.25-0.40	0.45-0.70	0.80-1.10	1.30-1.75	1.85-2.70
Neureclipsis bimaculata	0.16-0.22	0.25-0.36	0.38-0.55	0.59-0.87	0.93-1.36
Diplectrona felix	–	0.24-0.32	0.56-0.64	0.80-1.04	1.29-1.52
Hydropsyche fulvipes	–	–	–	–	1.72-1.76
Hydropsyche instabilis	–	0.26-0.32	0.56-0.64	0.88-1.04	1.44-1.74
Hydropsyche siltalai	0.20-0.22	0.24-0.35	0.43-0.68	0.78-1.15	1.42-1.71
Hydropsyche pellucidula	–	0.33-0.41	0.59-0.71	0.96-1.12	1.44-1.80
Hydropsyche contubernalis	–	–	–	0.80-0.96	1.28-1.60
Hydropsyche angustipennis	–	0.34-0.41	0.48-0.65	0.75-1.10	1.24-1.70
Hydropsyche saxonica	0.20-0.25	0.30-0.45	0.55-0.74	0.84-1.15	1.40-1.80
Cheumatopsyche lepida	0.18-0.22	0.27-0.34	0.41-0.50	0.60-0.71	0.90-1.02
Tinodes waeneri	0.15-0.20	0.23-0.27	0.33-0.43	0.53-0.69	0.80-0.92
Tinodes rostocki	0.11-0.14	0.16-0.20	0.22-0.32	0.38-0.48	0.52-0.66
Ecnomus tenellus	–	0.26-0.29	0.36-0.46	0.57-0.73	0.80-1.02
*Philopotamus montanus**	0.198±0.002	0.283±0.003	0.518±0.010	1.002±0.013	1.514±0.014

*Head widths of *P. montanus* are means ± 95% CL.

POLYCENTROPODIDAE

There are two main descriptions of the population development and life history of *Polycentropus flavomaculatus* in Britain, one from a Dartmoor stream (Elliott 1968) and the other from a set of outdoor, artificial channels in Dorset (Bass et al. 1982). Life histories are somewhat difficult to reconstruct because most instars were present throughout the year, pupae were present for much of the year (for all but three months in Dorset), the adult flight period is long, and 1st instar larvae are under-represented in collections. Elliott (1968) found that some larvae appeared in the 1st instar in autumn and emerged as adults in the following summer (Fig. 175). Others, presumably derived from winter-hatching eggs, develop only as far as the 3rd instar by July (lower trend-line in Fig. 175) and complete their growth in the following autumn. These individuals overwinter as normal 5th instar larvae or "resting" larvae in pupal cases. In this way, part of the population takes one year and part about 16 months to complete its life cycle.

In the Waterston Channels in Dorset, Bass et al. (1982) found a rapidly-growing generation, going from 1st to 5th instar between July and September, raising the possibility of two generations per year in that situation. It seems that the life cycle of *P. flavomaculatus* is flexible (probably according to temperature and food supply) and poorly synchronised, with the possibility of generation times from less than six months to nearly two years. There is a widespread occurrence of two peaks of flight activity in light-trap captures throughout Great Britain (Crichton et al. 1978).

Little is known about the life histories of the localised species *Polycentropus irroratus* and *P. kingi*. *P. kingi* has been taken in light-traps in Wales (Crichton et al. 1978), where there was a single, well-defined peak of flight activity in August. Elliott (1968) took adults of this species in July, August and September.

In a study of *Plectrocnemia conspersa* in a small iron-rich stream in Sussex (Hildrew & Townsend 1982), evidence was obtained for a steady growth-trend and a one-year life cycle, in spite of the fact that all instars were present for most of the year (Fig. 176). Hildrew & Wagner (1992) collected egg masses of *P. conspersa* in July and August from a small stream in central Germany. There was an average of 440 ± 76 (mean ± 95% CL; range 150 –800) eggs per mass, laid in a single layer embedded in a jelly plaque applied closely to the surface of large emergent stones or pieces of wood. Individual eggs were oval and 0.39–0.47 mm in length and 0.20–0.34 mm wide (just before hatching). Egg masses were round to oval and an average mass (with 440 eggs) had a mean area of 0.56 cm^2. Eggs took 20 days to hatch (at 18 °C),

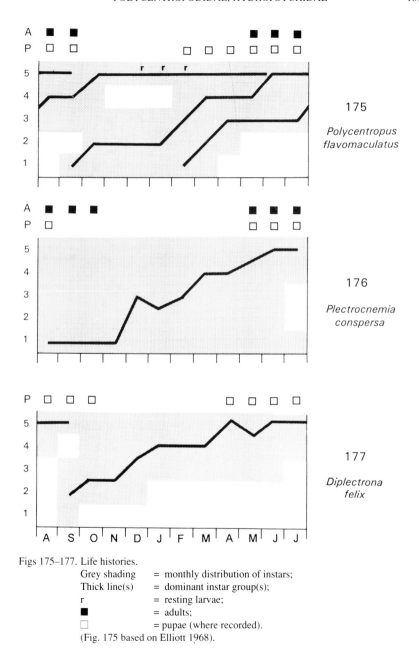

Figs 175–177. Life histories.
Grey shading   = monthly distribution of instars;
Thick line(s)   = dominant instar group(s);
r   = resting larvae;
■   = adults;
□   = pupae (where recorded).
(Fig. 175 based on Elliott 1968).

and there did not seem to be delayed hatching that could explain the prolonged presence of 1st instars in the field (more than 95% of eggs had hatched within 4 days). All of the newly hatched larvae spun silk around the natal egg mass and lived colonially for a few days, with as many as several hundred 1st instars in the same net. They did not feed for about the first 30 hours, but consumed residual yolk; thereafter they were predacious. Those obtaining an early meal rapidly moulted to the 2nd instar (within 7–10 days), became more aggressive to their siblings, and dispersed away from the net to lead independent lives. Those failing to obtain food remained as 1st instars for prolonged periods of time. It is not known if the remarkable phenomenon of the colonial net occurs in other Polycentropodidae.

The pattern of larval development illustrated in Fig. 176 agrees with light-trap catches from Scotland and northern England, which showed an extended flight-period from May until October, with a single peak in late July and early August (Crichton et al. 1978). In the south of England, however, there were two peaks of activity, one in late May and one in August. Since Tachet (1967) has demonstrated in the laboratory that larvae hatching from eggs in April can give rise to adults in September, it seems that two broods a year are possible. However, this was clearly not the case in the iron-rich stream studied by Hildrew & Townsend (1982).

The flight-period of *P. geniculata* is from May to September, with a single July peak in Scotland and two peaks (June and August) in Wales and northern England (Crichton et al. 1978). Jones (1969) has recorded its emergence from May to September in North Wales.

No detailed information on *Holocentropus* life cycles is available from Britain. However, Higler (1978) has described the pattern of larval growth of *H. picicornis* and *H. dubius* from a canal in the Netherlands. Small larvae of both species appeared in July, but *H. dubius* then grew more rapidly and overwintered at a larger size. Growth in *H. picicornis* accelerated in spring, and the pupation and emergence of the two species probably occurred at much the same time. It appears that all individuals of both species completed the life cycle in one year. This staggering of life cycles could be significant as a means of reducing competition between the two species.

Little information is available on the life cycles of the three *Cyrnus* species found in Britain. *Cyrnus trimaculatus* has a simple one-year life cycle in the River Thames and a single summer flight-period with a peak in July and August (Crichton et al. 1978). The flight activity began earlier (May) and finished later (September) in southern England than further north. *C. flavidus* has a single flight-period from July to September, with a peak in late July.

Rossiter (1983) commented on the life cycle of *Neureclipsis bimaculata* in a lake outlet in North Wales. Eggs are laid in batches of between 300 and 500 beneath the water by females that fly to lake outlets in May to early August.

Eggs hatched in 10–16 days and development to the 2nd instar was rapid. Most larvae pupated between the following March to May, with emergence in June or July. Larval growth rates were very variable (hence instars 2 to 5 were present for most of the year) and some particularly slow growers remained as larvae through the summer, pupated in autumn and emerged in May or early June the following year (i.e. at about 2 years old). These adults made up the first of two emergence peaks (the second was in July) which consisted of large females who laid many eggs.

HYDROPSYCHIDAE

The life cycles of some British hydropsychids are well known. *Hydropsyche siltalai* has been studied in North Wales by Hynes (1961), on Dartmoor by Elliott (1968), in South Wales by Hildrew & Edington (1979), and in north-east England by Boon (1979). In all these areas the life cycle takes one year and there is a single flight-period. The species is also univoltine in the River Rhône (Tachet & Bournaud 1981; Bournaud et al. 1986). Fig. 179 illustrates the life cycle of *H. siltalai* from the River Usk in South Wales. Hatching of eggs began in June and July and there was some growth of larvae until November, by which time most larvae were in the 3rd instar. Growth was rapid from March onwards and pupation began in June.

The life history of *H. pellucidula* is known from South Wales (Hildrew & Edington 1979) and from north-east England (Boon 1979) and differs markedly from that of *H. siltalai*. In the River Usk we found that, although emergence of *H. pellucidula* occurred only slightly earlier than that of *H. siltalai*, larval growth in the late summer was very rapid and the bulk of the population overwintered in the 5th instar (Fig. 178). Thus although *H. pellucidula* has a one-year development with a single extended flight-period, the life cycle is staggered compared with that of *H. siltalai*. The possible ecological significance of this is discussed by Hildrew (1978), Hildrew & Edington (1979) and Boon (1979).

It was found that the larval growth of *H. siltalai* in the River Usk (Hildrew 1978) and *H. pellucidula* in the North Tyne (Boon 1979) was accelerated in the lower reaches of these rivers. This is commonly observed in hydropsychid populations (Rutherford & Mackay 1986). Further, Tachet & Bournaud (1981) and Bournaud et al. (1986) found that *H. pellucidula* actually has two generations per year in the Rhône near Lyon (as does *H. exocellata* and *H. contubernalis*). Also on continental Europe, *H. bulgaromanorum* has two generations per year in the Loire (Lecureuil et al. 1983), final instars being dominant in May (the "spring generation") and again in August (the "summer generation").

In South Wales, *H. instabilis* was found to have a pattern of growth and development very similar to *H. siltalai* (Hildrew & Edington 1979) (Fig. 180). Only fragmentary information is available on the life cycle of the remaining species of *Hydropsyche, H. angustipennis*. Adults in southern England were found to have a single flight-period from May to September with peak activity in late July (Crichton 1960; Crichton et al. 1978) although, in Germany, Matzdorf (1964) has recorded a double flight-period.

Monthly samples of *Diplectrona felix* larvae taken from a small wooded stream in South Wales suggested that a one-year life cycle was the normal pattern (Fig. 177), although a few individuals may have spent a second winter as 5th instar larvae. Daytime swarms of adults were observed in August. Jones (1969), using emergence traps in North Wales, recorded an emergence period from May until August with a peak in late June and early July. This species is not attracted to light traps.

The life history of *Cheumatopsyche lepida* in the River Leven, the lake outflow of Windermere, has been well described by Elliott (1986; Fig. 181). Adults emerged at night in late June and July. Ovaries were immature at first but mating took place almost immediately and gravid females were taken six days after the onset of emergence. The eggs were quite large (0.35–0.40 mm mean length, 0.18–0.26 mm mean width) and there were 400–500 eggs per female. Gravid females flew upstream and oviposited underwater, laying one large and one or two smaller egg masses. Eggs hatched after 9–15 days at 18–22 °C in flowing water. The 1st instar lasted only 4–7 days during which the larvae were positively phototactic and swam actively into the water column and drifted downstream. Swimming ceased just before the moult to the 2nd instar, after which all larval stages were negatively phototactic. Larval growth was rapid, attaining the 5th instar by October, at which stage the larvae overwintered. Elliott (1986) describes the nets as "rather loose, voluminous, funnel-shaped". Pupae were found from May to July and pupal cases were made of small sand grains cemented to large boulders. The pupal stage lasted 7–10 days at 15–20 °C. Pupae cut a small hole at the end of the case and swam to the water surface where the adults emerged. While *C. lepida* is clearly univoltine in the River Leven it may be bivoltine in France (Lapchin & Neveu 1979).

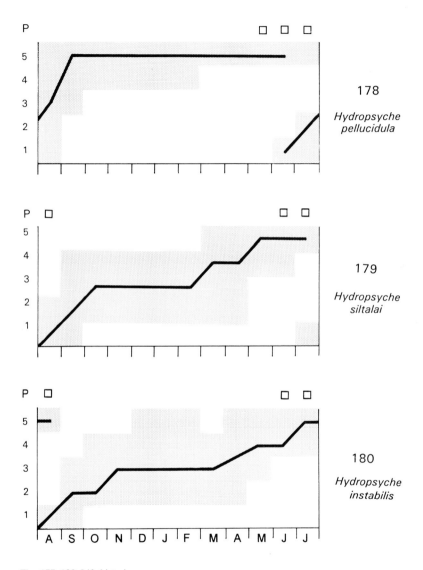

Figs 177--180. Life histories.
Grey shading   = monthly distribution of instars;
Thick line   = dominant instar group;
□   = pupae.
(After Hildrew & Edington 1979).

PHILOPOTAMIDAE

Elliott (1981) has, again, very thoroughly described the life cycle of *Philopotamus montanus* in an English Lake District stream. Oviposition occurred chiefly in May and June and took place during the day (most frequently between noon and early evening). Adults of both sexes dive down to the water surface and skip over it but females did not oviposit in this way. Rather, females walked down the side of a large stone and remained submerged for about 4–6 minutes. Masses of about 100 eggs were found and females possess sufficient for about three batches (number of eggs per female ranged from about 300 to 350). Hatching time for a small sample of eggs was 20–30 days at 12 °C. In the laboratory, larvae had moulted to the 2nd instar within about 14–18 days after hatching from eggs. First instar larvae were not taken in the field. All larvae had reached instar 4 or 5 by November (Fig. 182). Those in instar 5 built pupal cases, overwintered as "resting larvae" or prepupae, and pupated in spring. 4th instar larvae overwintered, grew rapidly in spring and pupated. Large numbers of 5th instar larvae were taken drifting downstream during the periods (March–May and September–November) when they were searching for pupation sites. Pharate adults (i.e. adults still in the pupal exuvium) emerged mainly at night. The life cycles of *P. montanus* in two other English Lake District streams were also univoltine, though there were modest variations. Females tended to fly upstream to oviposit in two of the three streams studied. Adults were found between April and June. Elliott's (1981) description of the life cycle of *P. montanus* is very unusual among studies on caseless caddis because it contains quantitative estimates of growth rate (which peaked in July/August at between about 6.0 and 7.5% dry weight day^{-1}) and mortality. The initial population had decreased by ca. 90% by the 2nd instar, and less than 0.4% laid eggs. The mean ratio of production to biomass (P/B) was about 3.7.

Rather little can be written about the other philopotamids. Jones (1969) caught adults of *Wormaldia occipitalis* in North Wales in every month of the year except December and January while Mackereth (1960) has suggested that *W. occipitalis* has a two-year life cycle in the English Lake District.

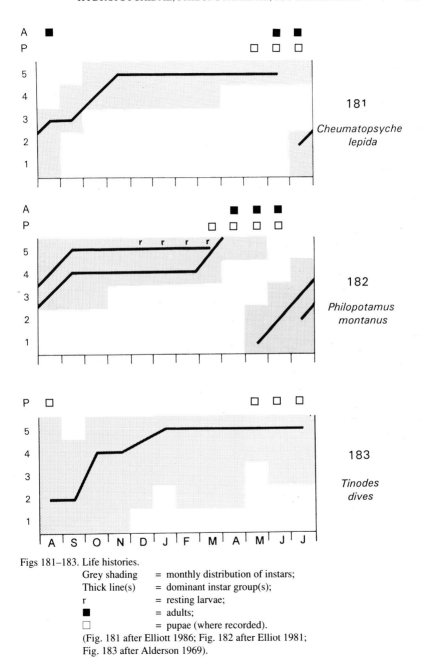

Figs 181–183. Life histories.

Grey shading	=	monthly distribution of instars;
Thick line(s)	=	dominant instar group(s);
r	=	resting larvae;
■	=	adults;
□	=	pupae (where recorded).

(Fig. 181 after Elliott 1986; Fig. 182 after Elliot 1981; Fig. 183 after Alderson 1969).

ECNOMIDAE

Light-trap catches of *Ecnomus tenellus* in the south of England showed it has a major peak of flight activity in July and a second smaller peak in late August (Crichton 1960; Crichton et al. 1978). A study of emerging adults by Jones (1976b) from a lake on Anglesey showed a single short emergence period.

PSYCHOMYIIDAE.

Most of our information about the life cycles of this family in Britain comes from unpublished work by Alderson (1969) and a study of *Tinodes waeneri* by Jones (1976a,b). Alderson found that in *T. dives* and *T. rostocki* development took one year (Figs 183, 184). Growth was continuous even during the winter months, and by January the population was dominated by 5th instar larvae. The life cycle of *T. rostocki* in a small, stony stream in central Germany was almost identical to that described for British populations (Becker 1993). In the uplands of South Wales, *Psychomyia pusilla* was also found to have a one-year life cycle, although in this case little growth took place until spring (Fig. 185). Alderson attributed this pattern to the dependence of the species on the spring bloom of diatoms.

Light-trap captures of *P. pusilla* showed a single peak of activity in July, in Scotland. In northern England and Wales a second peak occurs in late August, possibly indicating two generations a year in these localities (Crichton et al. 1978). The study by Jones (1976a) of the larval growth pattern of *T. waeneri*, in a lowland lake in North Wales, strongly suggests that there is a second generation in late summer (Fig. 186). This would account for the double emergence peak usually found in this species (Crichton 1960; Crichton et al. 1978). The quantitative study of *Tinodes waeneri* on the wave-washed shore of the eutrophic Lake Esrom in Denmark, by Dall et al. (1984), confirms a bivoltine life cycle. There were flight-periods in June and August. Larval growth rates peaked in August at 5.0 to 7.4% dry wt day^{-1} and the annual ratio of production to biomass (P/B) ratio for this bivoltine population was 5.73. On a sheltered shore of Lake Esrom, however, *T. waeneri* was univoltine (with a P/B ratio of 3.31) and at other localities there was a mixture of the two patterns. Hasselrot (1993) observed larvae inside their galleries, in still and stirred aquaria, and found that in the latter larvae spent more time feeding whereas in still water they fed less and ventilated their galleries more frequently, by undulating abdominal

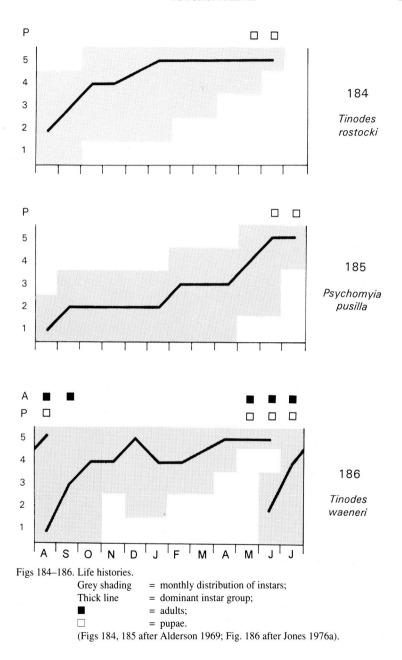

Figs 184–186. Life histories.
Grey shading   = monthly distribution of instars;
Thick line   = dominant instar group;
■   = adults;
□   = pupae.
(Figs 184, 185 after Alderson 1969; Fig. 186 after Jones 1976a).

movements. Such differences might account for differential growth and a protracted life cycle on sheltered shores.

Little information is available for the life cycles of other psychomyiids. Alderson (1969) found that *T. maclachlani* had a similar life cycle to that of *T. dives* and *T. rostocki*, whereas *T. unicolor* grew more slowly in winter and had a late emergence period in August and September.

RHYACOPHILIDAE

The study by Elliott (1968) of *Rhyacophila dorsalis* indicated that most individuals (middle trend-line in Fig. 187) completed their development in one year. However a smaller group, apparently hatching from eggs in winter, had grown only to the 3rd instar by July and did not reach the 5th instar until the following November (Fig. 187). These larvae built pupal cases but spent the winter in them as "resting larvae". Pupation took place from March onwards but adults did not emerge until May. In cases such as this it is unlikely that the larval groups are genetically isolated from one another, as variations in individual growth-rates would bring about exchanges between the groups. Adult *R. dorsalis* have been captured in light-traps as early as April, and as late as November (Crichton et al. 1978).

Elliott (1968) has shown that *R. munda* has a similar life cycle, in the sense of including one larval group that completes its development in a year, and another small group which takes nearly two years (Fig. 188). This smaller group probably hatches from eggs in spring and overwinters as 4th instar larvae.

The life cycle of the local species *R. septentrionis* has not been described in Britain, although adult records (Hickin 1967) indicate a flight-period from June to September. *R. obliterata* has been taken in light-traps between August and October in both England and Scotland, although the peak was about one month earlier in England. Hynes (1961) found that it overwintered as eggs or as 1st instar larvae.

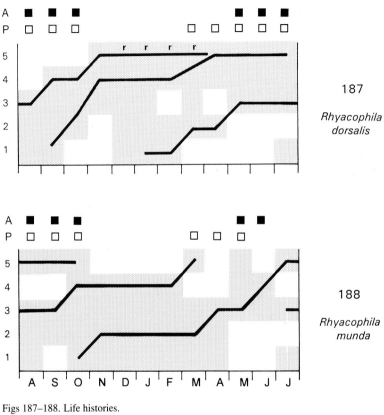

Figs 187–188. Life histories.

Grey shading   = monthly distribution of instars;
Thick line(s)   = dominant instar group(s);
r   = resting larvae
■   = adults;
□   = pupae (where recorded)
(After Elliott 1968).

ACKNOWLEDGEMENTS

We are grateful to the many people who have provided us with specimens or information for the preparation of this revised version of the key. Our colleagues from continental Europe have been especially helpful. Dr Henri Tachet kindly provided larvae of *Hydropsyche exocellata* from France, and Dr Johann Waringer and Dr Terje Bongard respectively sent us *Hydropsyche bulgaromanorum* from Austria and *Hydropsyche saxonica* from Norway.

In Britain, John Blackburn and Bruce Forrest helpfully provided specimens of *H. saxonica* and Dr Ian Wallace gave valuable advice about the incorporation into the key of the newly-discovered larvae of *Plectrocnemia brevis*. Dr Ann Edington gave vital assistance with field collecting and, along with Mrs A. J. Hutchinson, in the preparation of the typescript.

REFERENCES

Alderson, R. (1969). Studies on the larval biology of caddis flies of the family Psychomyiidae. Unpublished Ph.D. Thesis, University of Wales.

Alm, G. (1926). Beiträge zur Kenntnis der netzspinnenden Trichopteren-Larven in Schweden. *Int. Revue ges. Hydrobiol. Hydrogr.* **14**, 233-275.

Ambühl, H. (1959). Die Bedeutung der Strömung als ökologischer Faktor. *Schweiz. Z. Hydrol.* **21**, 133-264.

Badcock, R. M. (1949). Studies on stream life in tributaries of the Welsh Dee. *J. Anim. Ecol.* **18**, 193-208.

Badcock, R. M. (1975). The Hydropsychidae (Trichoptera) in Staffordshire. *N. Staffs. J. Field Stud.* **15**, 10-18.

Badcock, R. M. (1976). The distribution of the Hydropsychidae in Great Britain. In *Proc. 1st Int. Symp. Trichoptera, 1974*, 49-58. The Hague. Junk.

Badcock, R. M. (1977). The *Hydropsyche fulvipes – instabilis – saxonica* (Trichoptera) complex in Britain and the recognition of *H. siltalai* Döhler. *Entomologist's mon. Mag.* **113**, 23-29.

Barnard, P. C. (1985). An annotated check-list of the Trichoptera of Britain and Ireland. *Entomologist's Gaz.* **36**, 31-45.

Bass, J. A. B., Ladle, M. & Welton, J. S. (1982). Larval development and production by the net-spinning caddis, *Polycentropus flavomaculatus* (Pictet) (Trichoptera), in a recirculating stream channel. *Aquatic Insects* **4**, 137-151.

Becker, G. (1987). Net-building behaviour, tolerance and development of two caddisfly species from the River Rhine (*Hydropsyche contubernalis* and *H. pellucidula*) in relation to the oxygen content. *Oecologia* **73**, 242-250.

Becker, G. (1990). Comparison of the dietary composition of epilithic trichopteran species in a first-order stream. *Arch. Hydrobiol.* **120**, 13-40.

Becker, G. (1993). Age structure and colonization of natural substrata by the epilithic caddisfly *Tinodes rostocki* (Trichoptera: Psychomyiidae). *Arch. Hydrobiol.* **127**, 423-436.

Benke, A. C. & Wallace, J. B. (1980). Trophic basis of production among net-spinning caddisflies in a southern Appalachian stream. *Ecology* **61**, 108-118.

Berg, K. (1938). Studies on the bottom animals of Esrom lake. *K. danske Vidensk. Selsk. Skr.* **7**, 1-255.

Besch, W. K., Schreiber, I. & Herbst, D. (1977). Der Hydropsyche – Toxizitätstest erprobt an Fenethcarb. *Schweiz. z. Hydrol.* **39**, 69-85.

Besch, W. K., Schreiber, I. & Magnin, E. (1979). Influence du sulfate de cuivre sur la structure du filet des larves d'*Hydropsyche* (Insecta: Trichoptera). *Ann. Limnol.* **15**, 123-138.

Blackburn, J. H. & Forrest, M. B. (1995). New records of *Hydropsyche saxonica* McLachlan (Trichopt. Hydropsychidae) from small streams in Great Britain. *Entomologist's mon. Mag.* **131**, 71-76.

Bongard, T. (1990). Key to the Fennoscandian larvae of Arctopsychidae and Hydropsychidae (Trichoptera). *Fauna norv. Ser. B* **37**, 91-100.

Bongard, T., Arnekleiv, J. V. & Haug, A. (1991). *Hydropsyche saxonica* McLachlan, 1884 (Trichoptera, Hydropsychidae) new to Norway. *Fauna norv. Ser. B* **38**, 27-29.

Boon, P. J. (1978). The pre-impoundment distribution of certain Trichoptera larvae in the North Tyne river system (Northern England), with particular reference to current speed. *Hydrobiologia* **57**, 167-174.

Boon, P. J. (1979). Studies on the spatial and temporal distribution of larval Hydropsychidae in the North Tyne river system (Northern England). *Arch. Hydrobiol.* **85**, 336-359.

Boon, P. J. (1984). Habitat exploitation by larvae of *Amphipsyche meridiana* (Trichoptera: Hydropsychidae) in a Javanese lake outlet. *Freshwat. Biol.* **14**, 1-12.

Boon, P. J. (1987). The influence of Kielder Water on trichopteran (caddisfly) populations in the River North Tyne (Northern England). *Regulated Rivers: Research & Management* **1**, 95-109.

Bournaud, M., Tachet, H. & Perrin, J. F. (1982). Les Hydropsychidae (Trichoptera) du Haut-Rhone entre Geneve et Lyon. *Annls. Limnol.* **18**, 61-80.

Bournaud, M., Tachet, H. & Chessel, D. (1986). Distribution temporelle de six especes d'*Hydropsyche* sympatriques (Trichopteres) dans le Rhône. Coll. Nat. CNRS "Biologie des Populations", 600-608.

Brickenstein, C. (1955). Über die Netzbau der Larvae von *Neureclipsis bimaculata* (L.). *Abh. bayer. Akad. Wiss.* **69**, 1-44.

Brooker, M. P. & Morris, D. L. (1980). A survey of the macro-invertebrate fauna of the River Wye. *Freshwat. Biol.* **10**, 437-458.

Carmargo, J. A. (1991). Toxic effects of residual chlorine on larvae of *Hydropsyche pellucidula* (Trichoptera, Hydropsychidae): a proposal of biological indicator. *Bull. Environ. Contam. Toxicol.* **47**, 261-265.

Cooling, D. A. (1982). Records of Trichoptera from rivers in Southern England. *Entomologist's Gaz.* **33**, 123-134.

Crichton, M. I. (1960). A study of captures of Trichoptera in a light trap near Reading, Berkshire. *Trans. R. ent. Soc. Lond.* **112**, 319-344.

Crichton, M. I., Fisher, D. & Woiwood, I. P. (1978). Life histories and distribution of British Trichoptera, excluding Limnephilidae and Hydroptilidae, based on the Rothamsted Insect survey. *Holarct. Ecol.* **1**, 31-45.

Dall, P. C., Heegaard, H. & Fullerton, A. F. (1984). Life-history strategies and production of *Tinodes waeneri* (L.) (Trichoptera) in Lake Esrom, Denmark. *Hydrobiologia* **112**, 93-104.

Danecker, E. (1961). Studien zur hygropetrischen Fauna. Biologie und Ökologie von *Stactobia* und *Tinodes*. *Int. Revue ges. Hydrobiol. Hydrogr.* **46**, 214-254.

Darlington, S. T., Gower, A. M. & Ebdon, L. (1987). Studies on *Plectrocnemia conspersa* (Curtis) in copper contaminated streams in south west England. *Proc. 5th Int. Symp. on Trichoptera*, 353-357, W. Junk, Dordrecht, Netherlands.

Décamps, H., Besch, W. K. & Vobis, H. (1973). Influence de produits toxiques sur la construction du filet des larves d'*Hydropsyche* (Insecta: Trichoptera). *C.R. Acad. Sci. Paris* **276**, 375-378.

Dorier, A. & Vaillant, F. (1954). Observations et expériences relatives à la résistance au courant de divers invertébrés aquatiques. *Trans. Lab. Hydrobiol. Piscic. Univ. Grenoble* **45 & 46**, 9-31.

Dudgeon, D. (1987). A laboratory study of optimal behaviour and the costs of net construction by *Polycentropus flavomaculatus* (Insecta: Trichoptera: Polycentropodidae). *J. Zool., Lond.* **211**, 121-141.

Dunn, D. R. (1954). The feeding habits of some of the fishes and some members of the bottom fauna of Llyn Tegid (Bala Lake) Merionethshire. *J. Anim. Ecol.* **23**, 224-233.

Edington, J. M. (1964). The taxonomy of British polycentropid larvae (Trichoptera). *Proc. zool. Soc. Lond.* **143**, 281-300.

Edington, J. M. (1965). The effect of water flow on populations of net-spinning Trichoptera. *Mitt. int. Verein. theor. angew. Limnol.* **13**, 40-48.

Edington, J. M. (1968). Habitat preferences in net-spinning caddis larvae with special reference to the influence of water velocity. *J. Anim. Ecol.* **37**, 675-692.

Edington, J. M. & Alderson, R. (1973). The taxonomy of British psychomyiid larvae (Trichoptera). *Freshwat. Biol.* **3**, 463-478.

Edington, J. M. & Hildrew, A. G. (1973). Experimental observations relating to the distribution of net-spinning Trichoptera in streams. *Verh. int. Verein. theor. angew. Limnol.* **18**, 1549-1558.

Edington, J. M. & Hildrew, A. G. (1981). A key to the caseless caddis larvae of the British Isles with notes on their ecology. *Scient. Publs. Freshwat. Biol. Ass.* **43**, 1-91.

Edwards, R. W. & Brooker, M. P. (1982). *The Ecology of the Wye.* Monographiae Biologicae, 50. Junk, the Hague. 164 pp.

Elliott, J. M. (1968). The life histories and drifting of Trichoptera in a Dartmoor stream. *J. Anim. Ecol.* **37**, 615-625.

Elliott, J. M. (1981). A quantitative study of the life cycle of the net-spinning caddis *Philopotamus montanus* (Trichoptera: Philopotamidae) in a Lake District stream. *J. Anim. Ecol.* **50**, 867-883.

Elliott, J. M. (1986). Life cycle and growth of *Cheumatopsyche lepida* (Pictet) (Trichoptera: Hydropsychidae) in the River Leven. *Entomologist's Gazette* **37**, 45-49.

Englund, G. (1991). Asymmetric resource competition in a filter-feeding stream insect (*Hydropsyche siltalai*; Trichoptera). *Freshwat. Biol.* **26**, 425-432.

Englund, G. & Olsson, T. I. (1990). Fighting and assessment in the net-spinning caddis larva *Arctopsyche ladogensis*: a test of the sequential assessment game. *Anim. Behav.* **39**, 55-62.

Fey, J. M. (1993). Web and capture-net spinning activities of *Hydropsyche pellucidula* Curt. and *Hydropsyche contubernalis* McL. under artificial conditions (Trichoptera, Hydropsychidae). *Dtsch. ent. Z., N.F.* **40**, 319-331.

Fey, J. M. & Schumacher, H. (1978). Zum einfluss wechselnder Temperatur auf den Netzbau von Larven der Köcherfliegen – Art *Hydropsyche pellucidula* (Trichoptera: Hydropsychidae). *Entomologica Germanica* **4**, 1-11.

Fisher, D. (1977). Identification of adult females of *Tinodes* in Britain (Trichoptera: Psychomyiidae). *Syst. Ent.* **2**, 105-110.

Fox, H. M. & Sidney, J. (1953). Influence of dissolved oxygen on the respiratory movements of caddis larvae. *J. exp. Biol.* **30**, 235-237.

Fox, P. J. (1978). Caddis larvae (Trichoptera) as predators of fish eggs. *Freshwat. Biol.* **8**, 343-345.

Fritsch, F. E. (1950). *Phormidium incrustatum* (Naeg.) Gom., an important member of the lime encrusted communities of flowing water. *Biol. Jaarb.* **70**, 27-39.

Fuller, R. L. and Mackay, R. J. (1980). Feeding ecology of three species of Hydropsyche (Trichoptera: Hydropsychidae) in southern Ontario. *Can. J. Zool.* **58**, 2239-2251.

Gower, A. M. & Darlington, S. T. (1990). Relationships between copper concentrations in larvae of *Plectrocnemia conspersa* (Curtis) (Trichoptera) and in mine drainage streams. *Environmental Pollution* **65**, 155-168.

Gower, A. M., Myers, G., Kent, M & Foulkes, M. E. (1994). Relationships between macroinvertebrate communities and environmental variables in metal-contaminated streams in south-west England. *Freshwat. Biol.* **32**, 199-221.

Greenwood, M. T. & Hobday, C. (1988). The re-discovery of *Tinodes pallidulus* (McL.) (Trichopt., Psychomyiidae) in Britain. *Entomologist's mon. Mag.* **124**, 99-102.

Hart, D. D. (1983). The importance of competitive interactions within stream populations and communities. In *Stream Ecology* (Eds J. R. Barnes & G. W. Minshall), pp. 99-136. Plenum Press, New York.

Hasselrot, A. T. (1993). Insight into a psychomiid life. Ph.D. thesis, Uppsala University.

Hickin, N. E. (1950). Larvae of the British Trichoptera, 30. *Tinodes pallidula* McLachlan (Psychomyiidae). *Proc. R. ent. Soc. Lond. (A)* **25**, 103-106.

Hickin, N. E. (1953). *Tinodes pallidula* McLachlan (Trichoptera, Psychomyiidae). A second British station. *Entomologist* **86**, 113.

Hickin, N. E. (1954). Larvae of the British Trichoptera, 42. *Rhyacophila septentrionis* McLachlan (Rhyacophilidae). *Proc. R. ent. Soc. Lond. (A)* **29**, 59-61.

Hickin, N. E. (1967). *Caddis Larvae. Larvae of the British Trichoptera.* London. Hutchinson. 476 pp.

Higler, L. W. G. (1978). Observations on caddis larvae in *Stratiotes* vegetation. In *Proc. 2nd Int. Symp. Trichoptera, 1977*, 309-315. The Hague, Junk.

Hildrew, A. G. (1978). Ecological aspects of life history in some net-spinning Trichoptera. In *Proc. 2nd Int. Symp. Trichoptera, 1977*, 269-281. The Hague, Junk.

Hildrew, A. G. & Edington, J. M. (1979). Factors facilitating the coexistence of hydropsychid caddis larvae in the same river system. *J. Anim. Ecol.* **48**, 557-576.

Hildrew, A. G. & Morgan, J. C. (1974). The taxonomy of the British Hydropsychidae (Trichoptera). *J. Ent. (B)* **43**, 217-229.

Hildrew, A. G. & Townsend, C. R. (1976). The distribution of two predators and their prey in an iron-rich stream. *J. Anim. Ecol.* **45**, 41-57.

Hildrew, A. G. & Townsend, C. R. (1980). Aggregation, interference and foraging by larvae of *Plectrocnemia conspersa* (Trichoptera: Polycentropodidae). *Anim. Behav.* **28**, 553-560.

Hildrew, A. G. & Townsend, C. R. (1982). Predators and prey in a patchy environment: a freshwater study. *J. Anim. Ecol.* **51**, 797-815.

Hildrew, A. G. & Wagner, R. (1992). The briefly colonial life of hatchlings of the net-spinning caddisfly *Plectrocnemia conspersa. J. N. Am. Benthol. Soc.* **11**, 60-68.

Hildrew, A. G., Townsend, C. R. & Francis, J. E. (1983). Community structure in some southern English streams: the influence of species interactions. *Freshwat. Biol.* **14**, 297-310.

Hynes, H. B. N. (1961). The invertebrate fauna of a Welsh mountain stream. *Arch. Hydrobiol.* **57**, 344-388.

Jakob, U., Walther, H. & Klenke, R. (1984). Aquatic insect larvae as indicators of limiting minimal contents of dissolved oxygen. *Aquatic Insects* **6**, 185-190.

Jalón, D. G. de (1981). Description of *Hydropsyche* larvae found in the Iberian Peninsula. In *Proc. 3rd Int. Symp. Trichoptera, 1980*, 87-92. The Hague, Junk.

Jansson, A. & Vuoristo, T. (1979). Significance of stridulation in larval Hydropsychidae (Trichoptera). *Behaviour* **71**, 168-186.

Jenkins, R. A. (1977). Notes on the distribution of psychomyiid larvae (Trichoptera) in South-West Wales. *Entomologist's Rec. J. Var.* **89**, 57-61.

Jenkins, R. A. (1979). Records of Trichoptera from South-West Wales. *Entomologist's Gaz.* **30**, 31-43.

Joensuu, I. & Vuori, K.-M. (1993). The microhabitat selection by *Hydropsyche siltalai* and *H. contubernalis* caddis larvae at different densities. In *Proc. 7th Int. Symp. Trichoptera, 1992*, 211-212. Backhuys, Leiden.

Johnstone, G. W. (1964). Stridulation by larval Hydropsychidae. *Proc. R. ent. Soc. Lond. (A)* **39**, 146-150.

Jones, J. R. E. (1949). A further ecological study of the calcareous streams in the 'Black Mountain' district of South Wales. *J. Anim. Ecol.* **18**, 142-159.

Jones, J. R. E. (1950). A further ecological study of the River Rheidol; the food of the common insects of the main-stream. *J. Anim. Ecol.* **19**, 159-174.

Jones, N. V. (1969). The emergence of Trichoptera from a small ground-fed stream in North Wales. *Entomologist's mon. Mag.* **105**, 151-155.

Jones, N. V. (1976a). The Trichoptera of the stony shore of a lake with particular reference to *Tinodes waeneri* (L.) (Psychomyiidae). In *Proc. 1st Int. Symp. Trichoptera, 1974*, 117-130. The Hague. Junk.

Jones, N. V. (1976b). Studies on the eggs, larvae and pupae of *Tinodes waeneri* (L.). In *Proc. 1st Int. Symp. Trichoptera, 1974*, 131-143. The Hague, Junk.

Kaiser, P. (1965). Über Netzbau und Strömungssinn bei den Larven der Gattung *Hydropsyche* Pict. (Ins. Trichoptera). *Int. Revue ges. Hydrobiol. Hydrogr.* **50**, 169-224.

Kimmins, D. E. (1942). *Cyrnus insolutus* McL. (Trichoptera), new to Britain. *Entomologist* **75**, 66-68.

Kimmins, D. E. (1949). *Tinodes pallidula* McLachlan: an addition to the British list of Trichoptera. *Entomologist* **82**, 269-272.

Kimmins, D. E. (1953). A key to the European species of *Wormaldia*, with descriptions of two new species. *Ann. Mag. nat. Hist.* **6**, 801-808.

Kimmins, D. E. (1965). Keys to the British species of Rhyacophilidae and Philopotamidae. *Entomologist's Gaz.* **16**, 147-161.

Krawany, H. (1930). Trichopteren-Studien im Gebeit der Lunzer Seen. *Int. Revue ges. Hydrobiol. Hydrogr.* **23**, 417-427.

Lancaster, J., Hildrew, A. G. & Townsend, C. R. (1988). Competition for space by predators in streams: field experiments on a net-spinning caddis fly. *Freshwat. Biol.* **20**, 185-193.

Lapchin, L. & Neveu, A. (1979). Ecologie des principaux invertébrés filtreurs de la basse Nivelle (Pyrénées-Atlantiques). II. Hydropsychidae (Trichoptera). *Annls. Limnol.* **15**, 139-153.

Lecureuil, J. Y., Chovet, M., Bournaud, M & Tachet, H. (1983). Description, répartition et cycle biologique de la larve d'*Hydropsyche bulgaromanorum* Malicky 1977 (Trichoptera, Hydropsychidae) dans la Basse Loire. *Annls. Limnol.* **19**, 17-24.

Lepneva, S. G. (1956). Morphological relationships of the subfamilies Psychomyiinae, Ecnominae and Polycentropinae (Trichoptera) in the pre-imaginal stages. *Ent. Obozr.* **35**, 8-27. (In Russian).

Lepneva, S. G. (1970). *Fauna of the U.S.S.R. Trichoptera 1, Larvae and Pupae of Annulipalpia.* Translation from 1964 Russian edition. Jersulaim. Israel Program for Scientific Translations. 638 pp.

Macan, T. T. (1973). A key to the adults of the British Trichoptera. *Scient. Publs. Freshwat. Biol. Ass.* **28**, 1-151.

Mackereth, J. C. (1954). Taxonomy of the British species of the genus *Rhyacophila* (Trichoptera). *Proc. R. ent. Soc. Lond. (A)* **29**, 147-152.

Mackereth, J. C. (1960). Notes on the Trichoptera of a stony stream. *Proc. R. ent. Soc. Lond. (A)* **35**, 17-23.

Malas, D. & Wallace, J. B. (1977). Strategies for coexistence in three species of net-spinning caddis flies (Trichoptera) in second-order southern Appalachian streams. *Can. J. Zool.* **55**, 1829-1840.

Malicky, H. (1983). *Atlas of European Trichoptera.* The Hague, Junk. 298 pp.

Malicky, H. (1984). The distribution of *Hydropsyche guttata* Pictet and *H. bulgaromanorum* Malicky (Trichoptera: Hydropsychidae), with notes on their bionomics. *Entomologist's Gaz.* **35**, 257-264.

Malmqvist, B. (1993). A comparison of activity and giving-up-time in two species of *Rhyacophila* (Trichoptera). In *Proc. 7th Int. Symp. Trichoptera, 1992,* 257-260. Backhuys, Leiden.

Marshall, J. E. (1978). Trichoptera: Hydroptilidae. *Handbk Ident. Br. Insects* **1**, 14(a), 1-31.

Martin, I. D. & Mackay, R. J. (1982). Interpreting the diet of *Rhyacophila* larvae (Trichoptera) from gut analyses: an evaluation of techniques. *Can. J. Zool.* **60**, 783-789.

Matczak, T. Z. & Mackay, R. J. (1990). Territoriality in filter-feeding caddisfly larvae: laboratory experiments. *J. N. Am. Benthol. Soc.* **9**, 26-34.

Matzdorf, F. (1964). Beitrag zur Biologie von *Hydropsyche angustipennis* Curtis (Trich.). *Ent. Ber., Berlin* **2**, 73-79.

Moretti, G.P. (1983). *Tricotteri (Trichoptera) – Guide per il Riconoscimento delle Specie Animali delle Acque Interne Italiene.* Verona. Consiglio Nazionale delle Ricerche. 155 pp.

Mosely, M. E. (1939). *The British Caddis Flies (Trichoptera).* London. Routledge. 320 pp.

Nielsen, A. (1942). Über die Entwicklung und Biologie der Trichopteren mit besonderer Berücksichtigung der Quelltrichopteren Himmerlands. *Arch. Hydrobiol. (Suppl.)* **17**, 255-631.

O'Connor, J. P. (1977). Lough Derrygeeha, Co. Clare, a new locality for *Cyrnus insolutus* McLachlan (Trichoptera: Polycentropodidae). *Entomologist's Rec. J. Var.* **89**, 309-310.

O'Connor, J. P. & Good, J. A. (1984). *Tinodes dives* (Pictet): a caddisfly new to Ireland from Ben Bulben, Co. Sligo. *Entomologist's Rec.* **96**, 108-109.

O'Connor, J. P. & Wise, E. J. (1980). Larva of *Tinodes maculicornis* (Pictet) (Trichoptera: Psychomyiidae) with notes on the species' distribution and habitat in Ireland. *Freshwat. Biol.* **10**, 367-370.

Ormerod, S. J. (1984). Larvae of *Ecnomus tenellus* (Rambur) (Trichop., Ecnomidae) from a lake in mid-Wales. *Entomologist's mon. Mag.* **120**, 178.

Otto, C. (1985). Prey size and predation as factors governing the distribution of lotic polycentropodid caddisfly larvae. *Oikos* **44**, 439-447.

Otto, C. (1989). Effects of information asymmetries in contests between net spinning caddis larvae (*Plectrocnemia conspersa*). *Oecologia* **81**, 176-180.

Otto, C. (1993). Long-term risk sensitive foraging in *Rhyacophila nubila* (Trichoptera) larvae from two streams. *Oikos* **68**, 67-74.

Percival, E. & Whitehead, H. (1929). A quantitative study of the fauna of some types of stream-bed. *J. Ecol.* **17**, 282-314.

Petersen, L. B.-M. (1985). Food preferences in three species of *Hydropsyche* (Trichoptera). *Verh. Internat. Verein. Limnol.* **22**, 3270-3274.

Petersen, L. B.-M. (1987a). Field and laboratory studies of the biology of three species of *Hydropsyche* (Trichoptera: Hydropsychidae). Ph.D. thesis, University of Lund, Sweden.

Petersen, L. B.-M. (1987b). Direct observations of *Hydropsyche* prey selection. *Proc. 5th Int. Symp. Trichoptera, 1986*, 293-297. Dr W. Junk, Dordrecht, Netherlands.

Petersen, L. B.-M. & Petersen, R. C. Jr. (1983). Anomalies in hydropsychid capture nets from polluted streams. *Freshwat. Biol.* **13**, 185-191.

Petersen, L. B.-M. & Petersen, R. C. Jr. (1984). Effect of kraft pulp mill effluent and 4,5,6 trichloroguaiacol on the net spinning behaviour of *Hydropsyche angustipennis* (Trichoptera). *Ecological Bulletins* **36**, 68-74.

Petersen, R. C. (1986). Population and guild analysis for interpretation of heavy metal pollution in streams. In *Community Toxicity Testing* (Ed. J. Cairns Jr.), pp. 180-198. ASTM STP 920, American Society for Testing and Materials, Philadephia, P.A.

Petersen, R. C. Jr., Petersen, B.-M. & Wallace, J. B. (1984). Influence of velocity and food availability on catchnet dimensions of *Neureclipsis bimaculata* (Trichoptera: Polycentropodidae). *Holarctic Ecology* **7**, 380- 389.

Philipson, G. N. (1953a). The larvae and pupa of *Hydropsyche instabilis* Curtis (Trichoptera, Hydropsychidae). *Proc. R. ent. Soc. Lond. (A)* **28**, 17-23.

Philipson, G. N. (1953b). The larvae and pupa of *Wormaldia subnigra* (McLachlan) (Trichoptera, Philopotamidae). *Proc. R. ent. Soc. Lond. (A)* **28**, 57-62.

Philipson, G. N. (1954). The effect of water flow and oxygen concentration on six species of caddis fly (Trichoptera) larvae. *Proc. zool. Soc. Lond.* **124**, 547-564.

Philipson, G. N. (1969). Some factors affecting the net-spinning of the caddis fly *Hydropsyche instabilis* Curtis (Trichoptera: Hydropsychidae). *Hydrobiologia* **34**, 369-377.

Philipson, G. N. (1978). The undulatory behaviour of larvae of *Hydropsyche pellucidula* Curtis and *Hydropsyche siltalai* Döhler. In *Proc. 2nd Int. Symp. Trichoptera, 1977*, 241-247. The Hague, Junk.

Philipson, G. N. & Moorhouse, B. H. S. (1974). Observations on ventilatory and net-spinning activities of the larvae of the genus *Hydropsyche* Pictet (Trichoptera: Hydropsychidae) under experimental conditions. *Freshwat. Biol.* **4**, 525-533.

Philipson, G. N. & Moorhouse, B. H. S. (1976). Respiratory behaviour of larvae of four species of the family Polycentropodidae (Trichoptera). *Freshwat. Biol.* **6**, 347-353.

Pitsch, T. (1993). Zur Larvaltaxonomie, Faunistik und Ökologie mitteleuropäischer Fließwasser-Köcherfliegen (Insecta: Trichoptera). Ph.D. thesis, Technische Universität, Berlin. 316 pp.

Richardson, J. S. (1984). Effect of seston quality on the growth of a lake outlet filter feeder. *Oikos* **43**, 386-390.

Rossiter, A. (1983). The biology of *Neureclipsis bimaculata* (L.). Unpublished Ph.D. thesis, Unversity of Wales.

Roux, C., Tachet, M., Bournaud, M. & Cellot, B. (1992). Stream continuum and metabolic rate in the larvae of five species of *Hydropsyche* (Trichoptera). *Ecography* **15**, 70-76.

Rutherford, J. E. & Mackay, R. J. (1986). Variability in the life-history patterns of four species of *Hydropsyche* (Trichoptera: Hydropsychidae) in southern Ontario streams. *Holarctic Ecology* **9**, 149-163.

Ruttner, F. (1963). *Fundamentals of Limnology.* 3rd edn. Toronto. University of Toronto Press. 295 pp.

Sattler, W. (1958). Beiträge zur Kenntnis von Lebensweise und Körperbau der Larve und Puppe von *Hydropsyche* Pict. (Trichoptera) mit besonderer Berücksichtigung des Netzbaues. *Z. Morph. Ökol. Tiere* **47**, 115-192.

Sattler, W. (1963). Über den Körperbau und Ethologie der Larve und Puppe von *Macronema* Pict. (Hydropsychidae), ein als Larve sich von 'Mikro-Drift' ernährendes Trichopter aus dem Amazongebiet. *Arch. Hydrobiol.* **59**, 26-60.

Schofield, K., Townsend, C. R. & Hildrew, A. G. (1988). Predation and the prey community of a headwater stream. *Freshwat. Biol.* **20**, 85-96.

Schumacher, H. (1970). Untersuchungen zur Taxonomie, Biologie und Ökologie einiger Köcherfliegenarten der Gattung *Hydropsyche* Pict. (Insecta, Trichoptera). *Int. Revue ges. Hydrobiol. Hydrogr.* **55**, 511-557.

Scott, D. (1958). Ecological studies on the Trichoptera of the River Dean, Cheshire. *Arch. Hydrobiol.* **54**, 340-392.

Siltala, A. J. (1907). Über die Nahrung der Trichopteren. *Acta Soc. Flora Fauna fenn.* **29**, 1-34.

Silver, S. C. (1980). Ultrasound production during stridulation by hydropsychid larve (Trichoptera). *J. Zool.* **191**, 323-331.

Slack, H. D. (1936). The food of the caddis fly (Trichoptera) larvae. *J. Anim. Ecol.* **5**, 105-115.

Statzner, B. (1978). The effects of flight behaviour on the larval abundance of Trichoptera in the Schierenseebrooks (North Germany). In *Proc. 2nd Int. Symp. on Trichoptera, 1977,* 121-134. Junk, The Hague.

Stroot, P., Tachet, H. & Dolédec, S. (1988). Les larves d'*Ecnomus tenellus* et d'*E. deceptor* (Trichoptera, Ecnomidae): identification, distribution, biologie et écologie. *Bijdragen tot de Dierkunde* **58(2)**, 259-269.

Tachet, H. (1965). Récherches sur l'alimentation des larves de *Polycentropus* (Trichoptère) dans leur milieu naturel. *Annls Soc. ent. Fr., N.S.* **1**, 627-633.

Tachet, H. (1967). Quelques aspect du cycle biologique de *Plectrocnemia conspersa* (Curtis 1834) (Trichoptera, Polycentropodidae). *Annls Limnol.* **3**, 177-184.

Tachet, H. (1971a). Le filet-piège de la larve de *Plectrocnemia conspersa* (Trichoptères, Polycentropodidae). *Oecologia* **8**, 78-92.

Tachet, H. (1971b). Aspects descriptifs du comportement alimentaire chez la larve de *Plectrocnemia conspersa* (Trichoptera, Polycentropodidae). *Z. Tierpsychol.* **28**, 175-184.

Tachet, H. (1977). Vibrations and predatory behaviour of *Plectrocnemia* larvae (Trichoptera). *Z. Tierpsychol.* **45**, 61-74.

Tachet, H. & Bournaud, M. (1981). Cycles biologiques des Hydropsychidae et d'un Polycentropodidae (Trichoptera) dans le Rhône en amont de Lyon. In *Proc. 3rd Int. Symp. on Trichoptera, 1980*, 347-364.

Tachet, H., Pierrot, J. P. & Bournaud, M. (1987). Distribution of the *Hydropsyche* larvae and the structure of their nets. In *Proc. 5th Int. Symp. Trichoptera, 1986*, 281-286. Dr W. Junk, Dordrecht, Netherlands.

Tachet, H., Pierrot, J. P., Roux, C. & Bournaud, M. (1992). Net-building behaviour of six *Hydropsyche* species (Trichoptera) in relation to current velocity and distribution along the Rhône River. *J. N. Am. Benthol. Soc.* **11**, 350-365.

Townsend, C. R. & Hildrew, A. G. (1978). Predation strategy and resource utilization by *Plectrocnemia conspersa* (Curtis) (Trichoptera: Polycentropodidae). In *Proc. 2nd Int. Symp. Trichoptera, 1977*, 283-291. The Hague. Junk.

Townsend, C. R. & Hildrew, A. G. (1979). Form and function of the prey catching net of *Plectrocnemia conspersa* (Curtis) larvae (Trichoptera: Polycentropodidae). *Oikos* **33**, 412-418.

Townsend, C. R. & Hildrew, A. G. (1980). Foraging in a patchy environment by a predatory net-spinning caddis larva: a test of optimal foraging theory. *Oecologia* **47**, 219-221.

Townsend, C. R., Hildrew, A. G. & Francis, J. E. (1983). Community structure in some southern English streams: the influence of physicochemical factors. *Freshwat. Biol.* **13**, 521-544.

Vaillant, F. (1953). Les Trichoptères à larves hygropétriques. *Trav. Lab. Hydrobiol. Piscic. Univ. Grenoble* **45**, 33-48.

Vaillant, F. (1954). *Tinodes algirica* McLachlan, the hygropetric larvae of the *Tinodes* (Trichoptera). *Ann. Mag. nat. Hist.* **7**, 58-62.

Viedma, M. G. de & Jalón, D. G. de (1980). Descriptions of four larvae of *Rhyacophila (Pararhyacophila)* from the Lozoya River, Central Spain, and a key to the species of the Iberian Peninsula (Trichoptera: Rhyacophilidae). *Aquatic Insects* **2**, 1-12.

Vuori, K.-M. (1992). Hydropsychid caddis larvae as indicators of water pollution. *Ent. Tidskr.* **113**, 45-49.

Vuori, K.-M. (1994). Rapid behavioural and morphological responses of hydropsychid larvae (Trichoptera, Hydropsychidae) to sublethal cadmium exposure. *Environmental Pollution* **84**, 291-299.

Vuori, K.-M. (1995). Species and population specific responses of translocated hydropsychid larvae (Trichoptera: Hydropsychidae) to runoff from acid sulphate soils in the River Kyrönjoki, Western Finland. *Freshwat. Biol.* **33**, 305-318.

Wallace, I. D. & Wallace, B. (1983). A revised key to larvae of the genus *Plectrocnemia* (Polycentropodidae: Trichoptera) in Britain, with notes on *Plectrocnemia brevis* McLachlan. *Freshwat. Biol.* **13**, 83-87.

Wallace, I. D., Wallace, B. & Philipson, G. N. (1990). A key to the case-bearing caddis larvae of Britain and Ireland. *Scient. Publs. Freshwat. Biol. Ass.* **51**, 1-237.

Wallace, J. B. (1975). Food partitioning in net-spinning Trichoptera larvae: *Hydropsyche venularis, Cheumatopsyche etrona* and *Macronema zebratum* (Hydropsychidae). *Ann. ent. Soc. Am.* **68**, 463-472.

Wallace, J. B. & Malas, D. (1976). The fine structure of capture nets of larval Philopotamidae (Trichoptera): with special emphasis on *Dolophilodes distinctus*. *Can. J. Zool.* **54**, 1788-1802.

Wallace, J. B. & Merritt, R. W. (1980). Filter-feeding ecology of aquatic insects. *Ann. Rev. Ent.* **25**, 103-132.

Wallace, J. B. Webster, J. R. & Woodall, W. R. (1977). Role of filter feeders in flowing waters. *Arch. Hydrobiol.* **79**, 506-532.

Wesenberg-Lund, C. (1911). Biologische studien über den netzspinnenden Trichopteren larven. *Int. Revue ges. Hydrobiol. Hydrogr. (Biol. Suppl.)* **3**, 1-64.

Wiberg-Larsen, P. (1980). Bestemmelsesnøgle til larver af de danske arter af familien Hydropsychidae (Trichoptera) med noter om arternes udbredelse og økologi. *Ent. Meddr.* **47**, 125-140.

Wiberg-Larsen, P. (1993). Notes on the feeding biology of *Ecnomus tenellus* (Rambur, 1842). *Ent. Meddr.* **61**, 29-38.

Wiggins, G. B. (1982). Trichoptera. In *Synopsis and Classification of Living Organisms* (Ed. by S. P. Parker), pp. 599-612. New York. McGraw-Hill.

Williams, D. D., Cromer, G. L. & Williams, N. E. (1993). Structure of the trichopteran assemblage in a Welsh mountain stream: can temporal/spatial separations and food partitioning account for high diversity? In *Proc. 7th Int. Symp. Trichoptera, 1992*, 197-205. Backhuys, Leiden.

Williams, N. E. (1987). Caddis and quaternary palaeoecology – what have we learned so far? In *Proc. 5th Int. Symp. Trichoptera, 1986*, 57-60. Dordrecht, Junk.

Williams, N. E. & Hynes, H. B. N. (1973). Microdistribution and feeding of the net-spinning caddis flies (Trichoptera) of a Canadian stream. *Oikos* **24**, 73-84.

INDEX TO SPECIES

Page numbers in **bold** type refer to taxonomic aspects and those in plain type refer to ecological aspects. Changed specific names are shown in brackets [ ].

PUBLICATIONS OF THE FRESHWATER BIOLOGICAL ASSOCIATION

The Scientific Publications listed below are currently available. Prices of these and other publications of the FBA may be obtained from: Dept. DWS (Publications), Freshwater Biological Association, The Ferry House, Far Sawrey, Ambleside, Cumbria LA22 0LP, UK.

5. A KEY TO THE BRITISH SPECIES OF FRESHWATER CLADOCERA, by the late D. J. Scourfield & J. P. Harding, 3rd ed., 1966   ISBN 0 900386 01 0

13. A KEY TO THE BRITISH FRESH- AND BRACKISH-WATER GASTROPODS, by T. T. Macan, 4th ed., 1977.   ISBN 0 900386 30 4

17. A KEY TO THE ADULTS AND NYMPHS OF THE BRITISH STONEFLIES (PLECOPTERA) by H. B. N. Hynes, 3rd ed., 1977. (Reprinted 1993).   ISBN 0 900386 28 2

18. A KEY TO THE BRITISH FRESHWATER CYCLOPID AND CALANOID COPEPODS, by J. P. Harding & W. A. Smith, 2nd ed., 1974.   ISBN 0 900386 20 7

23. A KEY TO THE BRITISH SPECIES OF FRESHWATER TRICLADS, by T. B. Reynoldson, 2nd ed., 1978.   ISBN 0 900386 34 7

25. SOME METHODS FOR THE STATISTICAL ANALYSIS OF SAMPLES OF BENTHIC INVERTEBRATES, by J. M. Elliott, 2nd ed., 1977.   ISBN 0 900386 29 0

27. A KEY TO BRITISH FRESHWATER FISHES, by Peter S. Maitland, 1972.   ISBN 0 900386 18 5

29. TURBULENCE IN LAKES AND RIVERS, by I. R. Smith, 1975.   ISBN 0 900386 21 5

30. AN ILLUSTRATED GUIDE TO AQUATIC AND WATER-BORNE HYPHOMYCETES (FUNGI IMPERFECTI), by C. T. Ingold, 1975.   ISBN 0 900386 22 3

31. A KEY TO THE LARVAE, PUPAE AND ADULTS OF THE BRITISH DIXIDAE (DIPTERA), by R. H. L. Disney, 1975.   ISBN 0 900386 23 1

33. DEPTH CHARTS OF THE CUMBRIAN LAKES, by A. E. Ramsbottom, 1976.   ISBN 0 900386 25 8

34. AN ILLUSTRATED KEY TO FRESHWATER AND SOIL AMOEBAE, by F. C. Page, 1976.   ISBN 0 900386 26 6

35. A KEY TO THE LARVAE AND ADULTS OF BRITISH FRESHWATER MEGALOPTERA AND NEUROPTERA, by J. M. Elliott, 1977.   ISBN 0 900386 27 4

36. WATER ANALYSIS: SOME REVISED METHODS FOR LIMNOLOGISTS, by F. J. H. Mackereth, J. Heron & J. F. Talling, 1978 (Second Impression, 1989).   ISBN 0 900386 31 2

38. A KEY TO THE FRESHWATER PLANKTONIC AND SEMI-PLANKTONIC ROTIFERA OF THE BRITISH ISLES, by Rosalind M. Pontin, 1978.   ISBN 0 900386 33 9

39. A GUIDE TO METHODS FOR ESTIMATING MICROBIAL NUMBERS AND BIOMASS IN FRESH WATER, by J. Gwynfryn Jones, 1979.   ISBN 0 900386 37 1

41. A KEY TO THE BRITISH AND EUROPEAN FRESHWATER BRYOZOANS, by S. P. Mundy, 1980.   ISBN 0 900386 39 8

42. DESMIDS OF THE ENGLISH LAKE DISTRICT, by Edna M. Lind & Alan J. Brook, 1980.   ISBN 0 900386 40 1

44. A GUIDE TO THE MORPHOLOGY OF THE DIATOM FRUSTULE WITH A KEY TO THE BRITISH FRESHWATER GENERA, by H. G. Barber & E. Y. Haworth, 1981.
          ISBN 0 900486 42 8

45. A KEY TO THE LARVAE OF THE BRITISH ORTHOCLADIINAE (CHIRONOMIDAE), by P. S. Cranston, 1982.   ISBN 0 900386 43 6

46. THE PARASITIC COPEPODA AND BRANCHIURA OF BRITISH FRESHWATER FISHES: A HANDBOOK AND KEY, by Geoffrey Fryer, 1982.   ISBN 0 900386 44 4

47. A KEY TO THE ADULTS OF THE BRITISH EPHEMEROPTERA, by J. M. Elliott & U. H. Humpesch, 1983.   ISBN 0 900836 45 2

48. KEYS TO THE ADULTS, MALE HYPOPYGIA, FOURTH-INSTAR LARVAE AND PUPAE OF THE BRITISH MOSQUITOES (CULICIDAE), by P. S. Cranston, C. D. Ramsdale, K. R. Snow & G. B. White, 1987.   ISBN 0 900836 46 0

49. LARVAE OF THE BRITISH EPHEMEROPTERA: A KEY WITH ECOLOGICAL NOTES, by J. M. Elliott, U. H. Humpesch & T. T. Macan, 1988.   ISBN 0 900836 47 9

50. ADULTS OF THE BRITISH AQUATIC HEMIPTERA HETEROPTERA: A KEY WITH ECOLOGICAL NOTES, by A. A. Savage, 1989.   ISBN 0 900836 48 7

51. A KEY TO THE CASE-BEARING CADDIS LARVAE OF BRITAIN AND IRELAND, by I. D. Wallace, B. Wallace & G. N. Philipson, 1990.   ISBN 0 900386 49 5

52. BRITISH FRESHWATER CRUSTACEA: A KEY WITH ECOLOGICAL NOTES, by T. Gledhill, D. W. Sutcliffe & W. D. Williams, 1993.   ISBN 0 900386 53 3